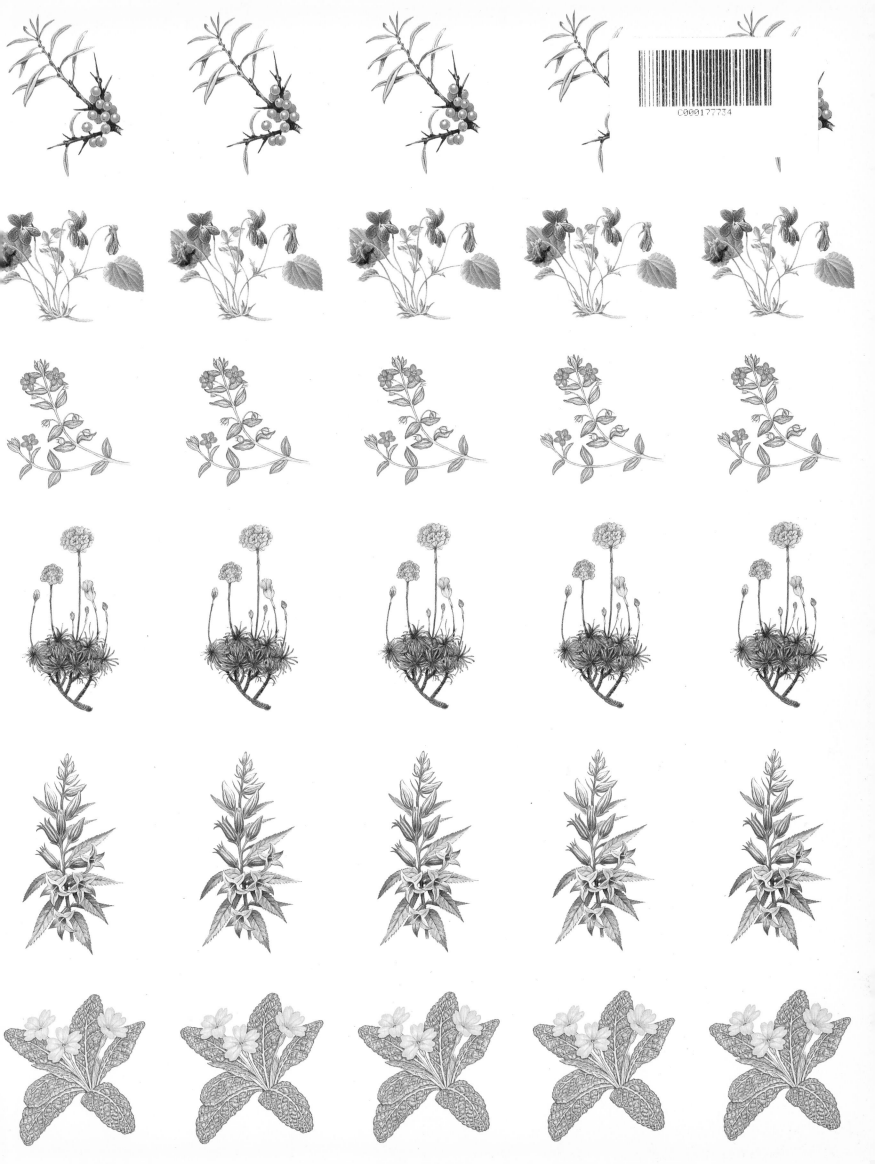

Pond in late summer with White Water-lily floating in the water. In the foreground (from left to right) are Common Reed, Meadowsweet, Purple Loosestrife, Hemp Agrimony and Bulrushes.

WILD flowers

of the
BRITISH ISLES
and
NORTHERN EUROPE

PAMELA
FOREY

PB

Parkgate Books

First Published in 1991

This edition published in 1997 by

Parkgate Books Ltd
London House
Great Eastern Wharf
Parkgate Road
London SW11 4NQ
Great Britain

1 3 5 7 9 8 6 4 2

British Library Cataloguing in Publication Data
Forey, Pamela
Wild Flowers of Britain and Northern Europe.
1. Northern Europe. Flowering Plants
I . Title
582.130948

ISBN 1 85585 367 1

Printed and bound in Italy

8–10 (twice as many as petals). **Rue fam. p. 86.**
☐Leaves simple and linear, opposite; stamens six, petals five. **Sea Heath fam. p. 96.**
☐Leaves simple, rounded to elliptical with long stalks, opposite, spirally arranged or in basal rosette; stamens 10 and petals five. **Wintergreen fam. p. 118.**

21 ☐Stamens five, alternating with petals, but also with five sterile stamens. **Flax fam. p. 82.**
☐Stamens 8–10, twice as many as petals. **22**

22 ☐Leaves borne in opposite pairs, simple and usually narrow. **Pink fam. p. 24.**
☐Leaves alternate, pinnately divided with simple leaflets jointed to stalk. **Wood Sorrel fam. p. 80.**
☐Leaves alternate or borne in dense rosettes, simple and often thick. **Saxifrage fam. p. 60.**

23 ☐Sepals two. **Purslane fam. p. 16, Poppy fam. p. 44.**
☐Sepals three or five. **Rockrose fam. p. 94.**

24 ☐Fruits single-seeded nutlets arranged in a ring cupped in the calyx (and sometimes in epicalyx too). **Mallow fam. p. 90.**
☐Fruits a cluster (not a ring) of single-seeded achenes, or in pods, or fleshy. **25**

25 ☐Petals three. **Crowberry fam. p. 116, Water-plantain fam. p. 202.**
☐Petals four, five or more numerous. **26**

26 ☐Stipules present. **Rose fam. p. 62.**
☐Stipules absent. **27**

27 ☐Petals four, in the form of a cross; fruits siliquas, with two valves opening from below. **Mustard fam. p. 46.**
☐Petals five or more, or if four then not in the form of a cross. **28**

28 ☐Evergreen woody climber; fruit a berry. **Ivy fam. p. 98.**
☐Herbaceous plants; fruit a cluster of follicles or achenes. **29**

29 ☐Succulent plants, with thick, fleshy, entire leaves. Stamens as many as or twice as many as petals. **Stonecrop fam. p. 58.**
☐Plants not succulent and leaves usually lobed or divided. Stamens numerous. **Buttercup fam. p. 32.**

30 ☐Flowers bilaterally symmetrical. **Orchid fam. p. 220.**
☐Flowers more or less regular. **31**

31 ☐Flowers very small with tiny calyx and five petals, borne in umbels; fruits consist of two sections joined together across the top of a central axis. **Carrot fam. p. 102.**
☐Flowers not in umbels, or if they are, fruits not as above. **32**

32 ☐Stipules present; stamens numerous. **Rose fam. p. 62.**
☐Stipules absent or soon falling; stamens 10 or less. **33**

33 ☐Styles two. **Saxifrage fam. p. 60.**
☐Style one. **Dogwood fam. p. 98, Willowherb fam. p. 98.**

34 ☐Ovary superior. **35**
☐Ovary inferior. **49**

35 ☐Flowers regular. **36**
☐Flowers bilaterally symmetrical. **44**

36 ☐Flowers tiny, green and inconspicuous, in spikes. Stamens conspicuous with long filaments and large anthers. **Plantain fam. p. 162.**
☐Flowers not as above. **37**

37 ☐Flowers with five-lobed corolla and a five-part corona (formed of scales or appendages) between the petals and the stamens. Stamens five, either with anthers fused together around stigma, or anthers fused to stigma. Fruit is two pods. **Milkweed fam. p. 124.**
☐Flowers not as above. **38**

38 ☐Stamens twice as many as petals or petal-lobes. **Stonecrop fam.** (*Umbilicus*) **p. 58, Heath fam. p. 114.**
☐Stamens as many as petals or petal-lobes. **39**

39 ☐Stamens opposite petal-lobes. **40**
☐Stamens alternating with petal-lobes. **41**

40 ☐Sepals two, overlapping, free or united. **Purslane fam. p. 16.**
☐Sepals joined into a tubular calyx which has 5–10 ribs, expanding and becoming membranous at the top; styles five. **Sea Lavender fam. p. 122.**
☐Sepals joined into a tubular, toothed or lobed, often leafy, not membranous calyx (usually with five, sometimes up to nine lobes or teeth); style single. **Primrose fam. p. 118.**

41 ☐Fruit two or four nutlets. **Forget-me-not fam. p. 132.**
☐Fruit a follicle. **Dogbane fam. p. 124.**
☐Fruit a capsule. **42**

42 ☐Sepals free. **Bindweed fam. p. 130.**
☐Sepals joined into a five-lobed calyx. **43**

43 □Ovary one-celled. **Bogbean fam.** p. 124, **Gentian fam.** p. 124.
□Ovary two-celled. **Nightshade fam.** p. 148.
□Ovary three-celled. **Diapensia fam.** p. 116, **Phlox fam.** p. 130.

44 □Flower with four petals, outer two spurred, joined at tips, inner two often joined; stamens two, each one divided into three. Brittle plants with watery juice. **Fumitory fam.** p. 42.
□Flower not as above. **45**

45 □Flowers pea-like, with a five-lobed calyx and a corolla formed of a large standard petal at the back, two wing petals and two lower petals joined to form a keel. Fruit a pod. **Pea fam.** p. 70.
□Flowers not as above. **46**

46 □Flowers with five free sepals, three outer ones small, two large inner ones modified into coloured wings; and three petals joined together. **Milkwort fam.** p. 86.
□Flowers not as above. **47**

47 □Stems square in cross-section, at least near the top; fruit of four nutlets. **Vervain fam.** p. 136, **Mint fam.** p. 138.
□Stem round in cross-section; fruit a capsule. **48**

48 □Insectivorous plants with rosettes of soft, fleshy leaves; stamens two. **Butterwort fam.** p. 162.
□Plants not insectivorous; stamens four or five. **Figwort fam.** p. 150, **Acanthus fam.** p. 160.

49 □Flowers more or less regular. **50**
□Flowers markedly bilaterally symmetrical. **57**

50 □Flowers in four-sided heads, one flower on each side and one on top. **Moschatel fam.** p. 162.
□Flowers not as above. **51**

51 □Flowers in heads with involucre of bracts beneath; fruits dry, one-seeded achenes. **52**
□Flowers not in heads as above, or if flowers in heads, then fruit a capsule. **53**

52 □Stamens two or four, free. **Teasel fam.** p. 170.
□Stamens five, anthers united around the style. **Daisy fam.** p. 173.

53 □Climbing plants with male and female flowers on separate plants. Stamens five, with two pairs joined by their filaments and one free. **Gourd fam.** p. 96.
□Flowers hermaphrodite, or if flowers unisexual, then plant not climbing. **54**

54 □Stamens twice as many as petals or petal-lobes. **Heath fam.** p. 114.

□Stamens as many as or fewer than petal-lobes. **55**

55 □Leaves alternate. **Bellflower fam.** p. 168.
□Leaves opposite or in whorls. **56**

56 □Stamens 1–3, inserted at base of five-lobed corolla. **Valerian fam.** p. 166.
□Stamens four, alternating with four petal-lobes. **Bedstraw fam.** p. 128.
□Stamens five, alternating with five petal-lobes. **Honeysuckle fam.** p. 164.

57 □Sepals three, petals three, one of them forming a lip. **Orchid fam.** p. 220.
□Flowers not as above. Sepals united to form a toothed calyx, or calyx forming a ridge; corolla two-lipped, with five lobes. **58**

58 □Fruit a capsule. **Bellflower fam.** (*Lobelia*) p. 168.
□Fruit a berry. **Honeysuckle fam.** (*Lonicera*) p. 164.
□Fruit a one-seeded nut. **Valerian fam.** p. 166.

59 □Perianth petal-like, of many similar whorls, petals gradually becoming smaller towards the centre of the flower. **Water-lily fam.** p. 38.
□Perianth petal-like, formed of two similar whorls not markedly different from each other. **60**

60 □Stamens numerous. **Buttercup fam.** p. 32.
□Stamens nine or less. **61**

61 □Ovary superior. **62**
□Ovary inferior. **63**

62 □Stamens nine; fruit formed of partly fused follicles. **Flowering Rush fam.** p. 202.
□Stamens six; fruit a capsule or berry. **Lily fam.** p. 206.

63 □Stamens one or two, borne with three stigmas on a special structure, the column; one petal forming a hanging lip. **Orchid fam.** p. 220.
□Stamens three. **Iris fam.** p. 216.
□Stamens six. **Daffodil fam.** p. 214.

64 □Aquatic plants with strap-shaped or ribbon-like leaves; male and female flowers borne in separate globular heads, males above and females below. **Bur-reed fam.** p. 232.
□Plants not as above. **65**

65 □Tall, marginal aquatic plants with thick, sword-shaped leaves and flowers in dense, green or brown, cylindrical spikes, males above and females below. **Bulrush fam.** p. 230.
□Plants not as above. **66**

66 □Plants with linear, grass-like leaves, often with

sheathing bases, flat or channelled in cross-section; flowers green or brown, individually small and inconspicuous, although often borne in conspicuous inflorescences. **67**

□Plants not as above; if leaves linear and grass-like, then flowers white or coloured and individually conspicuous. **68**

67 □Flowers in spikelets. **Sedge fam.** p. 232, **Grass fam.** p. 236.

□Flowers not in spikelets, but with sepal-like perianth segments and borne in spikes. **Arrow-grass fam.** p. 206.

□Flowers not in spikelets, but with membranous perianth segments and borne in heads or clusters. **Rush fam.** p. 218.

68 □Fully aquatic plants with submerged or floating leaves, flower spikes emerging from the water. **69**

□Land plants, or marginal aquatic plants with both leaves and flowers emerging from the water. **71**

69 □Leaves pinnately divided into fine, linear sections, usually borne in whorls of 4–6 (rarely 3–6). **Water-milfoil fam.** p. 100.

□Leaves simple and linear, borne in close whorls of 6–12. **Mare's-tail fam.** p. 100.

□Leaves simple, alternate or opposite, rarely in whorls of three. **70**

70 □Flowers unisexual, solitary or one male and one female borne together in a leaf axil. Leaves opposite; stipules absent. **Starwort fam.** p. 102.

□Flowers hermaphrodite in dense clusters or spikes on long stalks terminating the stems or growing from leaf axils. Leaves alternate with membranous sheathing stipules, or (rarely) leaves opposite and stipules absent. **Pondweed fam.** p. 204.

71 □Flowers in dense cylindrical spikes, either hermaphrodite and growing at an angle at the side of the stem; or unisexual with males at the top, females below and the spike sheathed in a spathe. **Arum fam.** p. 230.

□Flowers not as above. **72**

72 □Flowers minute; male and female flowers separate but on same plant, and consisting of one stamen and one carpel. **Spurge fam.** p. 88.

□Flowers not as above. **73**

73 □Woody shrubs. **74**

□Herbaceous or climbing plants. **76**

74 □Thorny shrubs with silvery-brown, scale-like hairs. **Oleaster fam.** p. 94.

□Shrubs not thorny, nor with silvery-brown hairs. **75**

75 □Male and female flowers on separate plants, borne in catkins; they have no sepals or petals. **Bog Myrtle fam.** p. 90.

□Hermaphrodite flowers with a brightly coloured calyx-tube which looks like a corolla. Petals absent. **Daphne fam.** p. 94.

76 □Climbing plants. **77**

□Herbaceous plants. **79**

77 □Flowers unisexual. **Hemp fam.** p. 14, **Yam fam.** p. 218.

□Flowers hermaphrodite. **78**

78 □Flowers bilaterally symmetrical, each with a rounded, swollen base, a long tube and an expanded tip. **Birthwort fam.** (*Aristolochia*) p. 40.

□Flowers regular, stipules sheathing. **Dock fam.** p. 18.

□Flowers regular, stipules absent. **Buttercup fam.** p. 32.

79 □Leaves with distinctive sheathing stipules (ochreae) at base of leaf stalk. **Dock fam.** p. 18.

□Stipules absent or not as above. **80**

80 □Flowers green and tiny, borne in spikes or in leaf axils, often dangling; male and female flowers often separate. **81**

□Flowers not green and tiny. **82**

81 □Stipules present. **Nettle fam.** p. 14, **Spurge fam.** (*Mercurialis*) p. 88.

□Stipules absent. **Amaranth fam.** p. 16, **Goosefoot fam.** p. 22.

82 □Petals free. **83**

□Petals fused into a lobed corolla. **84**

83 □Stamens numerous. **Buttercup fam.** p. 32.

□Stamens six, ovary superior. **Lily fam.** p. 206.

□Stamens six, ovary inferior. **Daffodil fam.** p. 214.

84 □Fruits are purple berries borne in hanging racemes. **Pokeweed fam.** p. 16.

□Fruits are small, green nuts crowned by remains of perianth segments. **Sandalwood fam.** p. 16.

□Fruits are capsules. **Birthwort fam.** (*Asarum*) p. 40.

NOTE: Page references within the main text following relate to those plants whose illustrations do *not* fall on the page facing their accompanying text.

Hemp family
Cannabaceae

A very small family, with only 2 genera and 4 species, but economically significant despite its small size. Hemp, *Cannabis sativa*, comes in several varieties, all yielding different products: fibres from one variety are made into rope and sailcloth; seeds from a second yield an oil used to make paints and soaps; resin extracted from the flowers and fruits of a third can be refined to produce hashish (known also as cannabis and marijuana) but this process is illegal. Hemp is widely cultivated in Europe and also grows wild as a casual weed.

Family features The flowers are unisexual and borne on separate plants in clusters in the leaf axils. Male flowers grow on stalks; each has a five-part perianth with overlapping sections, and five stamens. Female flowers are stalkless and borne in conspicuous, persistent bracts; each has an entire perianth enfolding a one-celled ovary. The fruits are achenes. The leaves are alternate or opposite, simple or palmately lobed, and they have stipules.

Hop, *Humulus lupulus*, is best known in its cultivated form, grown on leaning ropes in hop fields. The female flowers (the hops) are gathered in summer, dried and used in the manufacture of beer. In the Middle Ages beer was brewed without hops (when it was called ale) and its bitter flavour came from such plants as Ground Ivy (called Alehoof), Sage, or Yarrow. True beer (as opposed to ale) is made with hops, which were introduced into Britain from northern Europe; they give a bitter flavour to the beer and also help it keep longer. Hop flowers are also used in herb medicine, as a sedative and to improve digestion. Young hop shoots can be cooked and eaten as a vegetable—they taste like asparagus. Hop is a perennial climbing plant with bristly stems that twist in a clockwise direction. Its leaves are large and deeply lobed. Female flowers, like small yellow cones, grow in clusters in the leaf axils; they enlarge in fruit to form cones up to 1.5cm ($^1/_2$in) long, with papery bracts. Hops grow wild in hedges and thickets throughout Europe and Britain (especially in England and Wales), probably as escapes from cultivation in many areas.

Nettle family
Urticaceae

A family of herbs and small shrubs, with about 45 genera and 550 species, found throughout the world, but more common and with all the shrubs in the tropics. Many have stinging hairs. Some are noxious weeds. Others have fibres in their stems which are used for making fishing nets and cord, while some, like several *Pilea* species, are grown as house plants.

Family features The flowers are unisexual, very small and usually borne in clusters. They lack petals but have four or five calyx lobes, with the same number of stamens opposite the calyx lobes in male flowers and a superior ovary in female flowers. The fruits are achenes or drupes. The leaves are simple, opposite or alternate. Stipules are usually present.

Stinging Nettle, *Urtica dioica*, is the most familiar nettle, found in waste places, often near buildings and among rubble, on roadsides, in hedgerows and woods throughout the British Isles and Europe. It is a perennial plant which can spread to form extensive colonies. Its four-angled stems grow 100–120cm (3–4ft) tall, and bear opposite, toothed leaves. Stems and leaves are all covered with stinging hairs which leave a burning red rash on the skin if the plant is handled incautiously. In summer tiny, greenish flowers grow in branched clusters in the leaf axils, males and females on separate plants. Surprisingly, nettles are edible, although gloves must be worn for gathering them. The leaves cán be cooked as a green vegetable, like spinach, and are rich in vitamins and minerals.

The **Small Nettle**, *Urtica urens*, is a similar but smaller annual plant, growing only to 60cm (2ft) tall, with a single simple or branched stem. It has both male and female flowers on the same plant. This is a much more local species, growing in cultivated ground, arable land and waste places throughout Europe, mainly in the east in the British Isles.

Pellitory-of-the-wall, *Parietaria judaica*, is a branched perennial plant with soft, not stinging, hairs. It has sprawling, often reddish stems up to 40cm (15in) tall, and alternate, lance-shaped or ovate leaves. Dense clusters of flowers grow in the leaf axils, female flowers terminating the clusters and male flowers at the sides. This plant grows in old walls, in cracks between rocks and in hedge banks, locally throughout much of the British Isles (except in northern Scotland) and in western and southern Europe.

Mind-your-own-business or Mother-of-thousands, is usually known by its old Latin name of *Helxine soleirolii*. It may be grown as a house plant but is more often planted in patios, usually to the regret of the owner when it invades the flower beds, and comes up in every crack in the paths.

Mistletoe family
Loranthaceae

A family of shrubs which are semi-parasitic on trees. It contains about 30 genera and 400 species, found in tropical and temperate areas of the world.

Mistletoe, *Viscum album*, is one of only three species in this family found in Europe, and the only one in Britain. It is most familiar as the yellow-green plant with white berries used as decoration with holly at Christmas, but it has a long history in

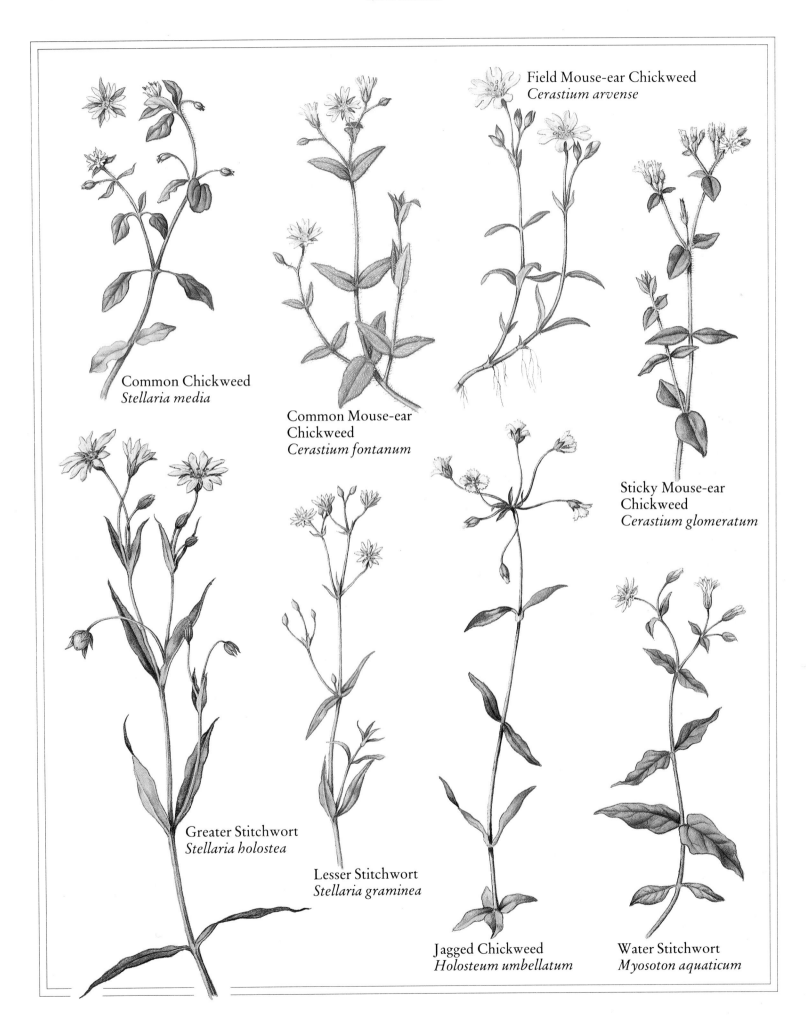

Common Chickweed
Stellaria media

Common Mouse-ear
Chickweed
Cerastium fontanum

Field Mouse-ear Chickweed
Cerastium arvense

Sticky Mouse-ear
Chickweed
Cerastium glomeratum

Greater Stitchwort
Stellaria holostea

Lesser Stitchwort
Stellaria graminea

Jagged Chickweed
Holosteum umbellatum

Water Stitchwort
Myosoton aquaticum

escapes to grow on walls and banks around towns and villages.

Jagged Chickweed, *Holosteum umbellatum* (p. 27), is more like the smaller mouse-ears. It is an annual plant, with a small clump of non-flowering shoots covered with greyish leaves, sticky on their upper surfaces. Flowering shoots grow up to 20cm (8in) tall and bear umbels of white flowers. This little plant grows in much of Europe in sandy or stony places, but is probably extinct in Britain. At one time it could be found on a few roofs or walls in East Anglia and Surrey.

Mouse-ears may be small plants but many members of this family are smaller, insignificant little plants with tiny, often inconspicuous flowers. **Pearlworts**, *Sagina* species, carry this tendency to an extreme. They are tiny mat-forming plants, with green tangled stems and linear leaves, the whole plant no more than a few centimetres across and 10cm (4in) tall.

Procumbent Pearlwort, *Sagina procumbens*, is a perennial weed that grows in damp places, often in lawns and paths in gardens, in damp arable land and beside streams. Although small, it seeds profusely, spreading slowly but surely and can soon cover large areas if left to its own devices. It produces tiny, greenish flowers on long stalks in the leaf axils, each flower with four sepals and often lacking petals. The plant grows throughout much of Europe and the British Isles. Knotted Pearlwort, *S. nodosa*, is similar in form and also grows in damp places, but it has larger, white flowers. Its name comes from the short side shoots which grow in the axils of the leaves, giving the stems a 'knotted' appearance.

There are several **Sandworts** in the genus *Minuartia*, which resemble the pearlworts in appearance. They are mat-forming plants with opposite, linear leaves and white flowers. However, they tend to be rare or local plants confined to specific habitats, like the Spring Sandwort, *M. verna*, which grows among base-rich rocks and on screes in suitable places throughout Europe. In Britain it is mostly confined to North Wales, the Lake District, the Peak District and the Pennines. Mossy Cyphel, *M. sedoides*, forms mossy, yellow-green cushions formed of densely leafy shoots. It grows on rocks and screes in the Highlands of Scotland, in the mountains of the Scottish islands and in the Alps, Pyrenees and Carpathians.

Thyme-leaved Sandwort, *Arenaria serpyllifolia*, is somewhat similar in appearance to Common Chickweed. It is an annual plant, untidy and sprawling, sometimes prostrate, with many stems and tiny, opposite, pointed-ovate leaves. However, it is wiry and rough to the touch, not succulent and not edible. Its white flowers have five uncleft petals. This plant is often found on bare ground, on roadsides and in waste places, in gardens and arable land, on walls, heaths and downs throughout the British Isles and Europe.

Sea Sandwort, *Honkenya peploides*, is a much larger species, a coastal plant found on beaches and sand-dunes all around the coasts of the British Isles and Europe; few plants grow in such conditions, and those that can are invaluable for stabilizing the sand. Sea Sandwort forms dense colonies with thick stems which run in and along the sand, frequently buried and then exposed by the shifting grains. Its stems have many fleshy leaves arranged in four overlapping ranks, and it bears small, whitish flowers in the axils of the leaves. Male and female flowers grow on separate plants, female flowers with minute petals. The succulence of the leaves is a common phenomenon in coastal plants, as in desert plants, for salt-laden soils are as difficult to extract water from as arid ones, and the leaves provide a means of storing water.

Corn Spurrey, *Spergula arvensis*, is an annual weed of arable and cultivated land on acid soils throughout the British Isles and Europe. It is also found on open ground in waste places and on roadsides. This plant is easy to spot, for it is distinctive, with slender green stems and fleshy, linear leaves which are opposite, but so divided that they look as if they are in whorls. It grows up to 40cm (15in) tall and in summer bears many terminal clusters of white flowers on thin stems.

Sand Spurrey, *Spergularia rubra*, has much-branched, often prostrate, stems and linear leaves. It is a small, usually annual plant, but individuals may survive for more than one year. It bears a few small pink flowers in clusters at the ends of the stems, the five petals of each flower alternating with the sepals and shorter than them. Sand Spurrey grows in lime-free, sandy or gravelly soils, on tracks and fields throughout Europe and Great Britain, and very locally in Ireland.

Lesser Sea-spurrey, *Spergularia marina*, is one of several succulent species growing in coastal areas. This one is found in salt marshes, along with Greater Sea-spurrey, *S. marginata*; both species may also be found on the sides of major roads treated with salt in winter. Lesser Sea-spurrey is a small, annual or biennial plant which forms prostrate mats of 20-cm (8-in) long fleshy stems with whorls of linear leaves, and terminal clusters of small pink, white-centred flowers. Greater Sea-spurrey is similar but a little larger, and a perennial plant, with pale pink or whitish flowers.

Rupturewort, *Herniaria glabra*, is another small plant, this one a mat-forming, annual species with numerous prostrate, branched stems growing about 15cm (6in) long and many tiny, elliptical leaves. It produces clusters of minute, pale pink flowers in the axils of the leaves on the side shoots. This is a rare and decreasing plant found in dry, sandy places in Europe north to southern Scandinavia, only in East Anglia and Lincolnshire in Great Britain.

Annual Knawel, *Scleranthus annuus*, is also a small annual, this one with sprawling, branched stems growing up to 25cm (10in) tall, and a spiky appearance coming from the narrow, pointed leaves. It flowers around midsummer, producing clusters of tiny, greenish, petal-less flowers hidden by bracts in the leaf axils. Annual Knawel grows in dry, sandy places, in waste places and cultivated land throughout Europe and Great Britain, locally in Ireland.

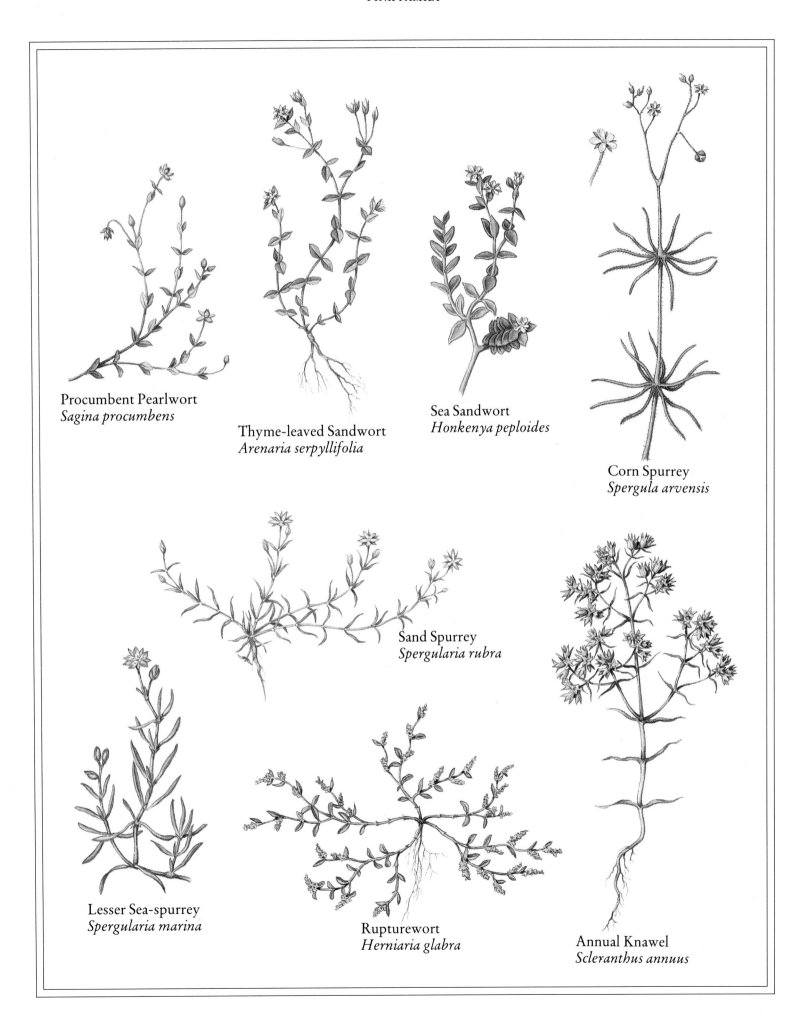

Procumbent Pearlwort
Sagina procumbens

Thyme-leaved Sandwort
Arenaria serpyllifolia

Sea Sandwort
Honkenya peploides

Corn Spurrey
Spergula arvensis

Sand Spurrey
Spergularia rubra

Lesser Sea-spurrey
Spergularia marina

Rupturewort
Herniaria glabra

Annual Knawel
Scleranthus annuus

Many of the **Campions** and **Catchflies**, members of the genera *Silene* and *Lychnis*, are similar to the Stitchworts but some of them are very much showier plants. There are about 300 *Silene* and 15 *Lychnis* species, the majority found in temperate areas of the world. Some are grown in gardens, but most are found only in the wild.

Red Campion, *Silene dioica*, must be one of the most attractive of these plants. It forms a short-lived perennial clump, with numerous non-flowering shoots about 20cm (8in) tall and many flowering shoots up to 90cm (3ft) tall in early summer. The shoots bear opposite pairs of soft, hairy leaves and many rose-red flowers with cleft petals protruding from sticky-hairy calyx tubes. Male and female flowers are separate. The flowers brighten a variety of habitats, mainly woods and hedgerows, but also limestone screes and coastal cliffs, usually in nutrient-rich places, throughout much of Europe and the British Isles, less commonly in Ireland.

The **White Campion**, *Silene alba*, is a similar but sticky-hairy plant, with pointed leaves and white flowers, slightly scented in the evening. It is found in hedgerows and grassy places, cultivated and waste land, most commonly in lowland areas and is probably not native to the British Isles, having been introduced from Europe in the Stone Age. It grows throughout Europe. White Campions and Red Campions hybridize freely, producing offspring with flowers in a variety of shades of pink. All the plants are fertile and it is often difficult to decide to which species they belong.

The **Bladder Campion**, *Silene vulgaris*, is a perennial plant, growing up to 1m (3ft) tall and found in a variety of disturbed habitats, in waste places and beside railway tracks, on roadsides and in cultivated land, in rough grassland and hedgerows throughout the British Isles and Europe. It forms a clump of erect, branched stems and opposite, pointed, lance-shaped leaves. Terminating the stems in early summer are many branched clusters of distinctive, nodding flowers. They have swollen, veined, bladder-like calyces enclosing the lower half of each flower, and the deeply cleft petals seem to emerge from the 'bladder' at all sorts of odd angles, so that the flowers often look vaguely dishevelled. The capsules that follow are globular, each with six teeth at the top; they are enclosed by the persistent calyces. The Sea Campion is a sprawling or cushion-forming subspecies of this plant with prostrate stems, *S. vulgaris* subsp. *maritima*. It rarely grows more than 20cm (8in) tall and may be found on cliffs, in sandy places and on shingle banks on the coasts of western Europe and the British Isles. It is often grown in rock gardens.

Nightflowering Catchfly, *Silene noctiflora*, is an annual plant found in sandy or chalky soils in arable land in southern and eastern England, much more rarely in western England and Scotland, very rarely in Ireland. It is also found through much of Europe. It has soft, downy hairs on its sticky-glandular stems and scattered hairs on the pointed, lance-shaped leaves. It bears few flowers and these have deeply cleft, white or pinkish petals which remain rolled inwards during the day, opening and spreading outwards at night, when their scent attracts moths. The calyx of each flower is somewhat swollen and egg-shaped, sticky and woolly in texture; it swells and remains around the egg-shaped capsule, which often bursts through as it enlarges in seed.

Small-flowered Catchfly, *Silene gallica*, is another sticky, annual species with small white or pink flowers in the axils of the leaves. It grows on sandy, arable land and in waste places, but is decreasing in numbers and is now confined to England and Wales in Britain, although plants are still found in much of continental Europe. The similar Sand Catchfly, *S. conica*, was never common and is becoming rare, found in sand-dunes and sandy or chalky fields in East Anglia. It has distinctive, very swollen calyces around the capsules.

Moss Campion, *Silene acaulis*, is a different sort of plant—a perennial, tufted, alpine species found on ledges, screes and mountain tops in Scotland, North Wales and the Lake District in Britain, and in the mountains of western Europe. It forms dense cushions of short stems with linear leaves, studded with deep rose-pink flowers in late summer. It is sometimes grown in troughs or rock gardens.

Another rock garden plant, one much more widely grown, is **Red German Catchfly**, *Lychnis viscaria*. In the wild in Europe it grows in sandy places and dry meadows, but in Britain it is rare and found in only a few places in Wales and Scotland, growing on igneous rocks. It forms perennial tufts of sticky, lance-shaped leaves from which grow erect flowering stems in early summer, reaching about 30–60cm (1–2ft) in height. They bear clusters of bright rose-pink flowers in the axils of the upper, linear leaves.

The related **Ragged Robin**, *Lychnis flos-cuculi*, is very different in appearance and in range. It is a perennial plant, with sprawling, leafy non-flowering shoots and erect flowering shoots growing to about 75cm (30in) tall and bearing their distinctive 'ragged', rose-red flowers around midsummer. Their appearance comes from the way that the petals are dissected into many linear segments. This attractive plant grows in damp meadows and marshes, wet woods and fens throughout the British Isles and Europe.

Corncockle, *Agrostemma githago*, was a common cornfield weed at one time but is now considered rare because of the improved techniques of seed screening and the use of herbicides. When the seeds of this plant were mixed with wheat, the resulting contaminated flour was poisoned by toxic glycosides present in the Corncockle seeds. The plant is an attractive one—an annual with erect stems 1m (3ft) tall, opposite, linear leaves and large, reddish-purple flowers in early summer. It is still found throughout Europe, while in Britain it is now most often found in waste places and on roadsides in lowland areas of England and Wales.

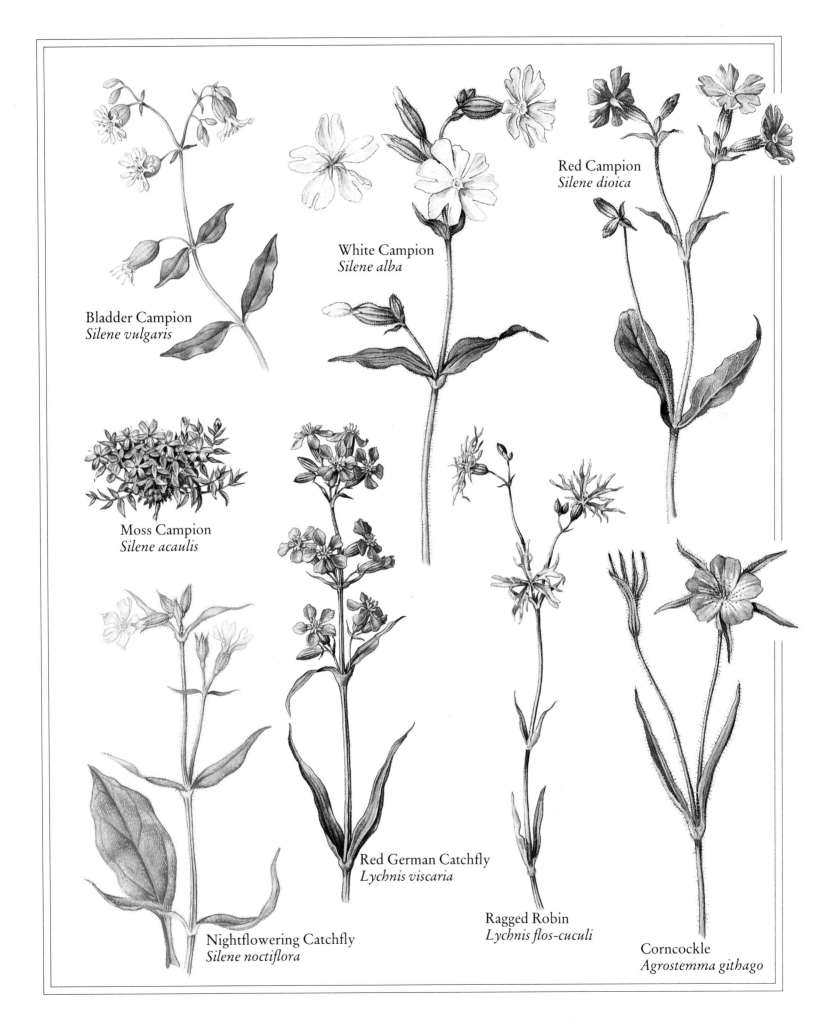

Bladder Campion
Silene vulgaris

White Campion
Silene alba

Red Campion
Silene dioica

Moss Campion
Silene acaulis

Red German Catchfly
Lychnis viscaria

Ragged Robin
Lychnis flos-cuculi

Nightflowering Catchfly
Silene noctiflora

Corncockle
Agrostemma githago

Buttercup family
Ranunculaceae

A family of herbs, shrubs and climbers, with about 50 genera and 1900 species found mostly in temperate and Arctic areas of the northern hemisphere. Some species have given rise to spectacular garden plants like delphiniums and clematis, or to interesting ones like anemones, hellebores and columbines.

All members of the buttercup family are poisonous. Buttercups, anemones and others are acrid and poisonous when fresh, causing ulceration and inflammation at the least and may cause diarrhoea, kidney damage and convulsions; poisoning is most common in livestock. When dried in hay the plants lose their toxicity since the alkaloids break down during drying. Other plants, like monkshoods, are much more poisonous and can cause death by heart failure.

Family features The flowers may be solitary or in terminal inflorescences. They are hermaphrodite and regular with all the parts free. There are 5–8 sepals in each flower, often overlapping, often falling, sometimes petaloid. Frequently there are five petals but they may be absent or numerous; usually they are overlapping and often each has a nectary at the base. The stamens are numerous and may be petaloid. The superior ovary is made up of one to many carpels and the fruits are usually either pod-like or achenes. The leaves are usually alternately arranged or may grow in a basal clump and they are often compound or divided. Stipules are usually absent.

There are about 14 **Monkshoods**, *Aconitum* species, in Europe. They are distinctive perennial plants with underground tubers, clumps of large, palmately-cleft leaves and flowering stems up to 1m (3ft) tall, bearing showy blue or yellow flowers, usually in late summer. The flowers have five petal-like sepals, the uppermost forming a helmet-shaped hood and concealing two nectaries, remnants of the petals. The flowers are followed by groups of 2–5 pods with many seeds.

The rhizomes of the plant usually known simply as **Monkshood**, *Aconitum napellus*, have been used for many years in commercial medicine and homoeopathy. They contain an alkaloid which is a painkiller and which reduces fever; monkshood is thus useful for treating rheumatism, inflammations and feverish colds. However, the plant is so poisonous that it can only be used under strict medical supervision. It has erect stems, palmately lobed leaves divided into linear segments and blue-mauve flowers in early summer followed by clusters of pods. In this species the hood in the flowers is broader than long and the nectary spurs are straight. Monkshood grows in damp mountain meadows and woods throughout much of Europe, except in the north, but is not common in Britain, found only in southwestern England and Wales.

Wolfsbane, *Aconitum vulparia*, is also found in much of Europe growing in damp mountain woods and meadows, but is absent from the British Isles. It forms clumps of palmately three-lobed leaves with erect flowering stems in summer; the flowers are yellow, with elongated, conical-cylindrical hoods and spirally twisted nectary spurs. It may be grown in gardens.

Larkspurs, members of the genus *Consolida*, are annual plants with much-divided leaves and racemes of distinctive flowers. Each flower is bilaterally symmetrical, with five outer petal-like sepals, the uppermost prolonged into a spur, and two inner petals joined together and forming a nectar-producing spur which is concealed within the sepal spur. The flowers are followed by many-seeded pods. There are about 12 species in Europe, found mostly in the Mediterranean area. None grow wild in the British Isles.

Forking Larkspur, *Consolida regalis*, grows in arable land and waste places across most of continental Europe. Its erect stems grow 1m (3ft) tall and end in showy racemes of light or dark blue flowers above leaves divided into linear lobes. Larkspur, *C. ambigua*, is the species most often grown in gardens. It usually has deep blue flowers, although cultivated varieties come in white, blue and pink forms. Wild plants originally come from the Mediterranean region.

Stinking Hellebore or Bear's-foot, *Helleborus foetidus*, is one of several hellebores that grow wild in Europe. It is sometimes grown in gardens along with its cousins, the Christmas Rose, *H. niger*, and Lenten Roses (garden hybrids of a variety of *Helleborus* species). Stinking Hellebore is a foetid perennial plant, with several leafy stems which persist over the winter, dying back when the new young stems appear above ground in late spring. The leaves are dark green and palmately lobed with narrowly lance-shaped, toothed segments. In early spring the pale green, bell-shaped flowers appear above the leaves and contrast vividly with the leaves. They grow in drooping, one-sided clusters and each one has a purple rim. The clusters of wrinkled green pods that follow remain on the plant for months. It grows wild in woods and rocky places in western and southern Europe, in southern and western England, and Wales, but may also be found in other parts of Britain and Europe where it has become naturalized.

Winter Aconite, *Eranthis hyemalis*, is another winter-flowering plant, but a much smaller one. It has tuberous underground rhizomes from which grow erect stems no more than 15cm (6in) tall, each with a ruff of three leaves beneath a single yellow, buttercup-like flower. The basal leaves appear after the flowers, each one rounded in outline and palmately lobed, dying down by early summer at the same time as the pods split open to release the seeds. This plant is native to the Mediterranean but is grown beneath trees in parks and gardens all over Europe and Britain, and has escaped in many areas to grow semi-wild in open, shady places.

Marsh Marigold or Kingcup, *Caltha palustris*, is a hairless, perennial plant only 60cm (2ft) tall. It forms a clump of long-stalked, dark green leaves with large, heart-shaped blades.

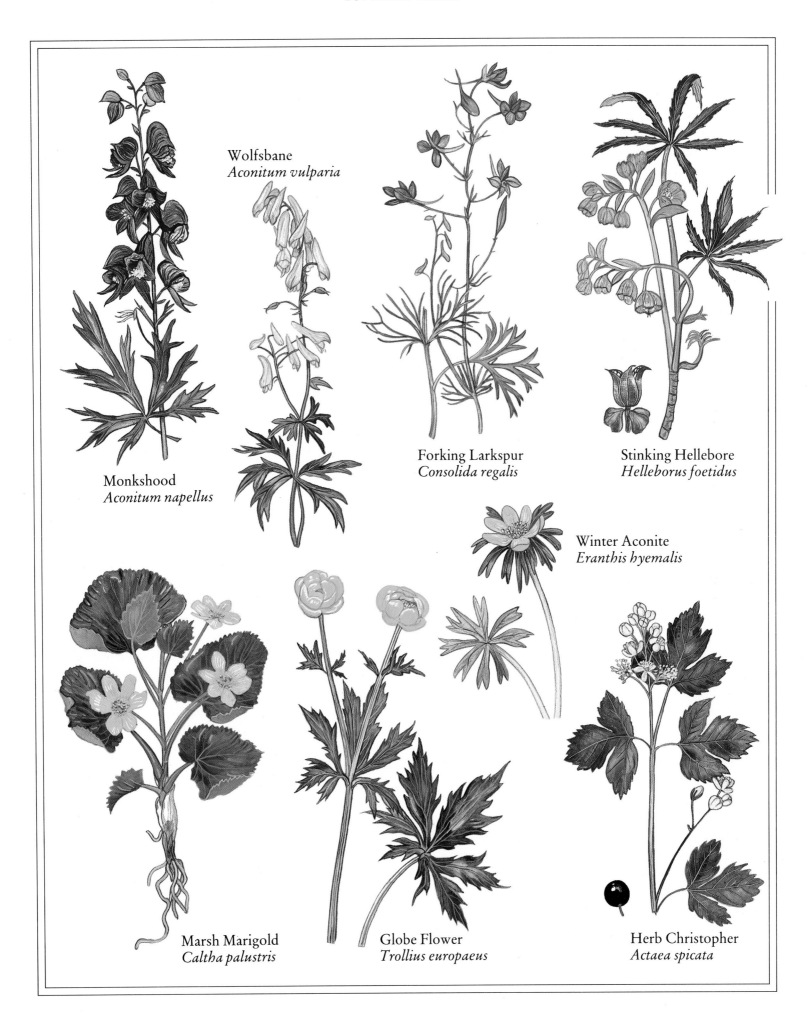

Wolfsbane
Aconitum vulparia

Monkshood
Aconitum napellus

Forking Larkspur
Consolida regalis

Stinking Hellebore
Helleborus foetidus

Winter Aconite
Eranthis hyemalis

Marsh Marigold
Caltha palustris

Globe Flower
Trollius europaeus

Herb Christopher
Actaea spicata

Roadside flowers in July with arable land in the background, the wheat just beginning to ripen. In the foreground (from left to right) are Field Poppies, Scentless Mayweed, Fumitory, Charlock and Chicory.

Mustard family
Cruciferae

Also known as **Brassicaceae**. There are about 375 genera and 3200 species of herbs in this family, found throughout the world, but mainly in the north temperate regions. This is an important family with many crop plants, including cabbage and broccoli, kale, turnip and swede, watercress and mustard. Rape is now grown on a wide scale for the oil extracted from its seeds. Other members of the family, like alyssum, aubrieta and wallflowers, are ornamental plants for the garden, which transform the flower beds in spring. Some, like Shepherd's Purse, are familiar weeds of gardens, waste and arable land.

Family features The regular, hermaphrodite flowers are distinctive, with four separate petals in the shape of a cross alternating with four separate sepals. Each flower has six stamens and a superior ovary. The flowers grow in racemes. Fruits are specialized capsules called siliquas (known familiarly as pods), with two valves opening from below, exposing a central septum to which seeds are attached. The leaves are alternate and lack stipules.

The genus *Brassica* is one that has produced many of the most important crop members of the family. *Brassica oleracea* has produced cabbages, cauliflowers, broccoli, Brussels sprouts and kale; *B. rapa* is the turnip; *B. napus* has produced rape and swede; *B. nigra* has produced black mustard. At one time White Mustard and the wild Charlock were also included in this genus, as *B. hirta* and *B. kaber* respectively, but modern botanists usually place them in a separate genus, *Sinapis*.

Wild Cabbage, *Brassica oleracea*, is a maritime plant in its truly wild state, growing on cliffs on the coasts of France, Spain and Italy, southern England and Wales. Elsewhere plants are likely to be naturalized forms of cultivated cabbages. This is a biennial or perennial plant, with a strong tap root and a thick sprawling stem which becomes woody and scarred with the leaf bases of old leaves. The leaves are thick, hairless and pinnately lobed or with wavy margins, grey and cabbage-like in appearance. The flowers are borne in an erect, lengthening inflorescence, opening over a long period in summer and followed by cylindrical, beaked fruits.

Black Mustard, *Brassica nigra*, has long been cultivated for its seeds. These are used to make the kitchen condiment and also in herb medicine to make mustard plasters and as an emetic. Mustard flour, made from the ground seeds, is an excellent deodorizer and antiseptic. The plant grows wild in waste places and on roadsides, beside streams and ditches, and on coastal cliffs throughout Europe. In Britain it is most common beside streams in England and Wales, and it also grows in southern Scotland and southern Ireland. This is an annual plant, with a much-branched stem growing up to 1m (3ft) tall. It has large, bristly, lobed lower leaves and smaller, toothed upper leaves, all with stalks. The flowers are bright yellow and are followed by upright, quadrangular pods pressed closely against the stems. Each pod has strongly keeled valves, a short beak and constrictions between the dark red-brown seeds.

Field Mustard, *Brassica rapa*, is a wild plant belonging to the same species as the turnip, but wild plants usually lack the swollen roots of the cultivated varieties. They grow in waste places and on cultivated land, beside streams and ditches throughout Europe and the British Isles. This is an annual plant with an erect stem, lobed lower leaves and toothed upper ones. The flowers are bright yellow and the inflorescence is unusual in this family since it does not lengthen. The result is that open flowers on their long stalks overtop the still-closed buds in the centre of the inflorescence. The pods are held more or less erect and have long slender beaks.

Charlock or Wild Mustard, *Sinapis arvensis*, was at one time a serious weed of vegetable and grain crops, for it produced an abundance of seed which germinated so profusely that the weeds smothered large areas of the true crop. Sometimes wheat was not worth harvesting, for so much of the field had been taken over. In addition to competing with the crops for space, light and water, Charlock also acts as a host for insect and fungal pests which attack other cruciferous crop plants. With the advent of modern weedkillers, this species has become less of a menace; however, it may still be found in arable land, around the edges of fields and in waste places, especially in areas where the soil is heavy or calcareous. It grows throughout Europe, Great Britain and Ireland.

Charlock is an annual plant, with a stiffly hairy, erect stem and roughly hairy leaves. The lower leaves are coarsely toothed but upper ones become progressively simpler. The bright yellow flowers produce long, beaked pods held upright and away from the stem, each with 6–12 dark red-brown seeds. The seeds can be substituted for those of Black Mustard.

White Mustard, *Sinapis alba*, is grown for fodder, as a green manure and for its seeds which are made into mustard. The active ingredient of mustard is mustard oil, a substance that is highly irritant and poisonous in its pure form or in large quantities; condiment mustard is too strongly flavoured to be palatable in anything but small amounts. At one time mustard poultices were used as a remedy for rheumatism and chilblains, since they draw blood into an affected area, warming it and improving circulation. White Mustard grows as a weed of arable and waste land throughout Great Britain, Ireland and Europe, except in the extreme north. It is an annual plant, with an erect stem up to 80cm (30in) tall, stiffly hairy, pinnately lobed leaves and a lengthening inflorescence of bright yellow flowers followed by stiffly hairy, beaked capsules. These contain 1–4 yellowish or pale brown seeds.

Wild Radish or White Charlock, *Raphanus raphanistrum*, is a pernicious weed much disliked by vegetable farmers. It grows throughout Europe, in Great Britain and Ireland,

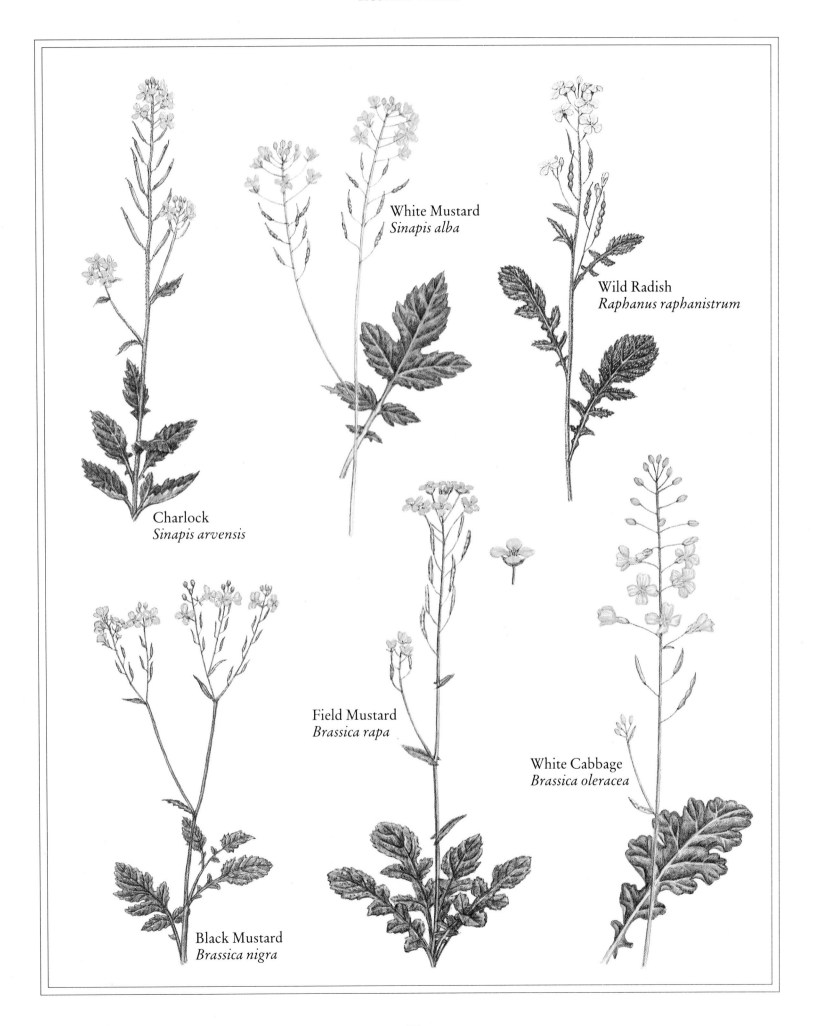

White Mustard
Sinapis alba

Wild Radish
Raphanus raphanistrum

Charlock
Sinapis arvensis

Field Mustard
Brassica rapa

White Cabbage
Brassica oleracea

Black Mustard
Brassica nigra

especially on calcareous soils. This is an annual plant, with rough, hairy stems, lobed leaves and yellowish flowers, becoming whiter with age. The petals have heavy mauve veins. Its fruits are distinctive—long cylindrical pods on ascending stalks, becoming ribbed and constricted between each seed as they dry out; eventually the pods break up and each seed is dispersed inside its section of pod. Wild Radish is related to garden radishes, the relationship becoming evident if garden plants go to seed, when they produce the same kind of pods.

Several members of this family are associated with the sea. **Seakale**, *Crambe maritima*, grows on shingle banks and sandy beaches, often on the drift line, or on cliffs and among rocks. It is not common, being restricted to suitable habitats, but is found all along the Baltic and Atlantic coasts of Europe, including those of Britain and Ireland. In Britain it is most common in the south. This plant is edible, the best parts being the young shoots which can be blanched and eaten like asparagus. It is a perennial, with a fleshy crown from which grow large clumps of leaves able to withstand burial in the shifting stones of the shingle. The leaves are blue-green, fleshy and pinnately lobed with a wavy outline. In summer the plant sends up erect stems ending in broad clusters of white flowers, followed by rounded fruits shaped like balloons.

Sea Rocket, *Cakile maritima*, is another maritime species, found on drift lines on shingle banks and sandy beaches around the coasts of Europe and the British Isles. It is an annual, with prostrate or sprawling, branched stems radiating outwards from a central tap root. The stems are leafy, with succulent, greyish leaves, varying in shape from pinnately lobed to entire. Purple flowers appear around midsummer in dense, terminal inflorescences; they are followed by stubby fruits.

Hare's-ear Cabbage, *Conringia orientalis*, grows as a casual weed of arable land and waste places in much of Europe, introduced from the southeast. It grows mostly near the coast in Britain. This annual plant has an erect stem up to 50cm (20in) tall, with characteristic leaves—elliptical with bases clasping the stem—and yellow-white flowers. The pods are elongated, curved and four-angled.

Wall Rocket, *Diplotaxis muralis*, is also known as Stinkweed, since it smells of rotten eggs if bruised. Coming originally from southeastern Europe, it now grows in limestone and chalk, on rocks and cliffs, old quarries and old walls throughout much of Europe, especially in southern England and Ireland in the British Isles. It is an annual or biennial, with a rosette of elliptical, often lobed leaves and one or more erect flowering stems in summer. The flowers are sulphur yellow, borne in an elongating inflorescence and followed by more or less erect fruits, each containing two rows of seeds. This feature serves to distinguish *Diplotaxis* species from many other cruciferous plants.

Perennial Wall Rocket, *Diplotaxis tenuifolia*, is a perennial plant; it lacks a rosette of leaves but has leafy stalks with deeply lobed leaves and yellow flowers in summer. It grows in old walls and waste places across much of Europe, except the north, and has been introduced in southern England.

The **Pepperworts** are members of the genus *Lepidium*, a variable group of annual to perennial plants, all with dense racemes of white flowers. There are 21 species in Europe. **Field Pepperwort**, *L. campestre*, is an annual, grey-green plant, with a branched, erect stem up to 60cm (2ft) tall. Its basal leaves are lyre-shaped but wither before flowering; the stem leaves are triangular with long basal lobes and they clasp the stem. The flowers are white and tiny, followed by rounded, notched fruits covered with white scales when mature. This plant grows in dry, grassy places, on roadsides and banks, in arable land and on walls throughout Europe and Great Britain; it is rare in Scotland and Ireland. The young shoots are edible, chopped up in salads like watercress, or added, with capers and gherkins, to mayonnaise for serving with fish.

Smith's Cress, *Lepidium heterophyllum*, is a greyish-hairy, perennial species, a smaller plant growing 45cm (18in) tall at most. It has a basal rosette of long-stalked, elliptical leaves that wither before flowering, and erect flowering stems with narrow, triangular leaves that have long basal lobes clasping the stem. The small, white flowers are followed by broadly winged, rounded, notched fruits that lack scales. This plant grows in dry, open places, in arable and waste land, and beside roads and railways throughout western Europe, Great Britain and in all but the northwest area of Ireland.

Swine-cress or Wart-cress, *Coronopus squamatus*, is a small, annual or biennial plant, with branched, prostrate stems and pinnately lobed leaves. The small white flowers grow in dense clusters in the leaf axils in summer and are followed by large, kidney-shaped, warty fruits, usually the first thing to catch the eye. This little plant grows in waste places, often on bare ground, throughout southern England, becoming rarer in the north, also in Ireland and throughout Europe. Lesser Swine-cress, *C. didymus*, is an introduced species from South America, a weed of cultivated land; it emits a sulphurous smell, has feathery leaves and pitted, rather than warty, fruits.

Hoary Cress, *Cardaria draba*, is another invader, this one from southeastern Europe, and a much more serious weed. It is a perennial plant which forms a spreading colony, smothering any other plants in its path. Its roots may penetrate to a depth of 3m (10ft) once it is well established, so that it becomes very difficult to eradicate. It is found in many parts of Europe, including much of Great Britain (most commonly in the south), and is scattered through Ireland. It grows in cultivated land, on roadsides, railway embankments and other disturbed places. Each shoot grows to about 90cm (3ft) tall, has hairy, deeply toothed leaves—those on the stem with clasping bases—and dense, umbel-like clusters of white flowers borne on long stalks in the upper leaf axils in early summer. The fruits are kidney-shaped and split into single-seeded sections.

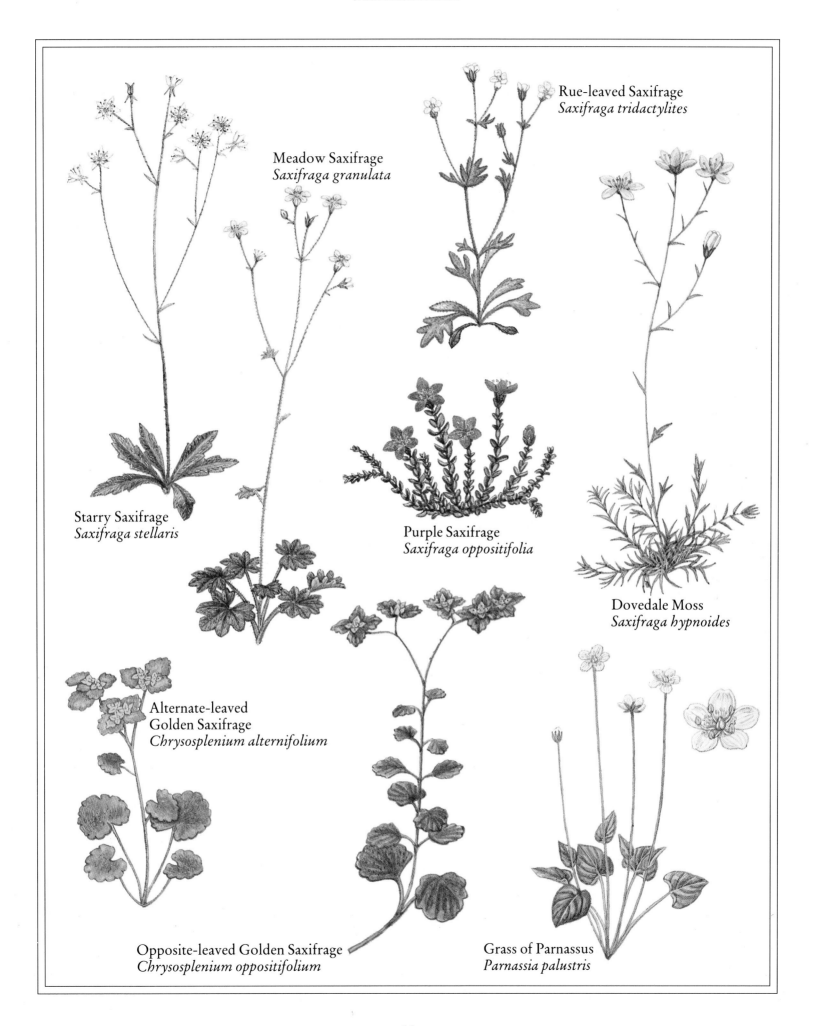

Meadow Saxifrage
Saxifraga granulata

Rue-leaved Saxifrage
Saxifraga tridactylites

Starry Saxifrage
Saxifraga stellaris

Purple Saxifrage
Saxifraga oppositifolia

Dovedale Moss
Saxifraga hypnoides

Alternate-leaved
Golden Saxifrage
Chrysosplenium alternifolium

Opposite-leaved Golden Saxifrage
Chrysosplenium oppositifolium

Grass of Parnassus
Parnassia palustris

Grass of Parnassus, *Parnassia palustris* (p. 61), grows in wet meadows, beside streams and lakes, in bogs and marshes across most of Europe and locally in Great Britain and Ireland. It is declining in numbers, however, and is probably extinct in parts of the south and Midlands. This perennial plant has a rosette of long-stalked, heart-shaped leaves and solitary white flowers on erect flowering stalks. Grass of Parnassus can be identified by the pattern of the stamens in each flower—five fertile stamens between the petals and five fringed sterile ones opposite the petals. There are many *Parnassia* species in the northern hemisphere; the stamens make them sufficiently distinctive to be placed by some botanists in a separate family of their own, the Parnassiaceae.

Rose family
Rosaceae

A large and important family, with about 100 genera and over 2000 species, found throughout the world, especially in the temperate regions. The family includes many fruit trees, such as apple, pear, cherry, peach and plum. Almond trees provide nuts. Other trees, like mountain ash and whitebeam, crab apple, hawthorn and ornamental cherry, are planted in city parks and streets, as well as in gardens. The family is also rich in shrubs, including the roses themselves, spiraeas, potentillas and cotoneasters. Herbaceous garden plants include geums, lady's mantles and strawberries.

Family features The flowers are hermaphrodite and regular, with five separate, often overlapping sepals and petals. The flowers have numerous stamens. The ovary is usually superior, with the floral parts in rings around its base, or it is inferior, with the floral parts in rings above it. The ovary has one to many carpels, variously free or united; the styles usually remain free. The fruits are achenes, drupes or pomes. The leaves are simple or compound, usually alternate, often with a pair of stipules attached to the leaf stalk.

Meadowsweet, *Filipendula ulmaria*, grows throughout Europe and the British Isles, often in abundance in wet meadows, fens and marshes, in wet woods and on the banks of rivers. It is a perennial plant, forming clumps of dark green, pinnate leaves and erect, leafy flowering stems 60–120cm (2–4ft) tall in summer. Each leaf has up to five pairs of large leaflets, with smaller leaflets between the larger ones. The flowers are small with creamy-white petals, sweetly scented and borne in clusters, with a fluffy appearance that comes from the long stamens. The fruits consist of several carpels which become twisted around each other, so that they look like spirals.

Dropwort, *Filipendula vulgaris*, grows in quite a different environment—in calcareous grassland, often on downs and limestone uplands, throughout much of Europe north to southern Norway. In the British Isles it is widespread only in England. This perennial plant forms clumps of pinnate leaves with many toothed leaflets, larger leaflets alternating with smaller ones. In summer it bears almost leafless flowering stems up to 80cm (2–3ft) tall, tipped with a spreading, flat-topped cluster of creamy white flowers opening from pink buds. The fruits are hairy and the carpels do not form a spiral.

Goatsbeard, *Aruncus dioicus*, is an impressive perennial plant, with several erect, leafy stems up to 2m (6ft) tall, topped in early to mid summer with plumes of white, fluffy flowers. It has large compound leaves up to 50cm (20in) long, with long stalks and pointed-oblong, serrated leaflets. The branched flower plumes have separate male and female flowers, the males with many stamens and the females with three carpels each. The plant grows in damp, shady places and woods in western and central Europe. It is grown in gardens in Britain.

Lady's Mantles belong to the large genus *Alchemilla*, with probably over 100 species in Europe. However, species are very difficult to distinguish in this genus, for Lady's Mantles produce seed without pollination (like hawkweeds), so there is no exchange of genes between individuals. In consequence the seeds from one individual form a closed population and could be said to be a species. These perennial plants have palmate or palmately lobed leaves and numerous flowers in branched cymes. The flowers are green or yellow-green, the colour coming from the calyx and epicalyx, for they lack petals.

Common Lady's Mantle, *Alchemilla vulgaris*, grows in damp grassland and woods, on stream banks and rocky ledges, especially on basic soils, throughout most of Europe and the British Isles. It is rare in southeastern England. It forms large clumps of attractive, palmately lobed leaves that hold drops of water after rain or heavy dew. The yellow-green flowers are less attractive, borne in large, branched clusters on leafy stalks in summer and followed by many seeds.

Alpine Lady's Mantle, *Alchemilla alpina*, is a mountain species, growing in grassland and in rock crevices, often on acid substrates, in the mountains throughout much of Europe, in Scotland and northern England, rarely in Ireland. It forms small clumps of palmately divided leaves with lance-shaped leaflets, dark green above and silvery-hairy beneath, growing on long stalks from a woody crown. The flowers are borne in small clusters on long stalks, often hidden between the leaves. This plant is sometimes grown in rock gardens.

Parsley Piert, *Aphanes arvensis*, grows on bare ground in arable land, gardens, waste places and roadsides, also in grassland and heaths throughout much of Europe and the British Isles. This is a very small, pale green, annual plant, often only 2cm (1in) tall. It has branched, sprawling stems covered with fringed, cup-like stipules and fan-shaped, lobed leaves, each lobe further divided into three sections. The flowers are tiny and petal-less, borne in dense clusters opposite the leaves, each cluster half cupped in one of the leafy stipules.

Goatsbeard
Aruncus dioicus

Meadowsweet
Filipendula ulmaria

Dropwort
Filipendula vulgaris

Parsley Piert
Aphanes arvensis

Alpine Lady's Mantle
Alchemilla alpina

Common Lady's Mantle
Alchemilla vulgaris

There are about 13 different **Avens**, *Geum* species, in Europe. **Water Avens**, *G. rivale*, is a wetland plant growing in wet meadows and marshes, in wet woods and beside streams, usually in shady places on base-rich soils. It forms a clump of compound pinnate leaves, each one with a very broad terminal leaflet. The flowers are borne on leafy flowering stems in loose terminal clusters; they are nodding, with purplish sepals and orange-pink petals. The centre of each flower, like those of all avens, contains many ovaries which enlarge into numerous achenes. In Water Avens the long styles are hooked in fruit, so that the fruit forms a burr which catches in fur or clothing.

Wood Avens or Herb Bennet, *Geum urbanum*, is a perennial plant forming a clump of hairy compound leaves; each leaf has 2–3 pairs of lateral leaflets and one large, lobed terminal leaflet. In early summer the small, yellow flowers appear in loose clusters on separate, leafy stalks 20–60cm (8in–2ft) tall. The fruits form hooked burrs, the hooks jointed and often pointing downwards. This plant grows in shady, damp places in woods and hedgerows throughout Europe and the British Isles, except the extreme north.

White Mountain Avens, *Dryas octopetala*, grows on sea cliffs and rocky grassland in the extreme north of Scotland and Europe, in mountain rock crevices and on ledges further south in its range. It is found in the mountains of Europe, Scotland, Ireland and northern England, rarely in Wales. It has prostrate, semi-woody stems and many dark green leaves, like miniature oak leaves but with pale undersides. White flowers grow on erect stalks in early summer and are followed by plumed achenes with white feathery styles. The plant is always attractive, in flower and in fruit, and even in winter for it is evergreen. It is sometimes grown in rock gardens.

Agrimony, *Agrimonia eupatoria*, grows in open woods and woodland edges, in hedgebanks, on roadsides and on the edges of fields throughout Europe and the British Isles, but rarely in northern Scotland. It forms an erect, leafy stem 30–60cm (1–2ft) tall, with dark green, compound leaves in which large leaflets are interspersed with small ones; the leaflets have toothed margins. In late summer a spike of small yellow flowers forms at the top of the stem. The fruits which follow are distinctive; each is top-shaped, with several rows of hooked bristles on its top surface—an aid to dispersal since they get tangled in the hair of passing animals.

Great Burnet, *Sanguisorba officinalis*, is an old herbal plant, highly astringent, used to stop internal bleeding and to check diarrhoea and dysentery. It has become much less common since its damp, grassland habitats have disappeared with modern farming methods. It is found throughout much of Europe, most commonly in England and Wales in Britain. It is a hairless perennial with a rosette of pinnate leaves. Each leaf has 3–7 pairs of long-stalked, toothed leaflets that become larger towards the tip. In summer the flowering stems appear, 30–100cm (1–3ft) tall, with a few similar leaves and dense, oblong heads of reddish flowers terminating the stems. The colour comes from the sepals for the flowers lack petals.

Salad Burnet, *Sanguisorba minor*, is a smaller plant found in calcareous grassland, usually on chalk and limestone uplands, across much of Europe. In Britain it is most common in England and Wales, occurring much more locally in Scotland and Ireland. It forms small, perennial clumps of pinnate leaves, each with 4–12 pairs of toothed leaflets. In summer the flowering stems grow about 60cm (2ft) tall, with pinnate leaves near the base and rounded flower heads at the top. Unlike the heads of Great Burnet, which has hermaphrodite flowers, those of Salad Burnet vary—female flowers with reddish styles at the top of each head, hermaphrodite ones in the centre and hermaphrodite or male flowers at the base. This plant smells of cucumber when bruised and the leaves can be added to punch.

Sibbaldia, *Sibbaldia procumbens*, is a very small, tufted, perennial plant, often only 3cm (1in) tall, with a rosette of long-stalked, three-lobed leaves. The leaves are hairy and the leaflets three-toothed at their tips. The tiny flowers are borne on separate stalks in dense, terminal clusters; their petals are narrow and yellowish, sometimes absent, smaller than the purplish calyces and epicalyces. This is a mountain plant found in high rock crevices and alpine pastures, in the mountains of northern and central Europe, also in the Highlands of Scotland and Cumbria. It is related to the Cinquefoils.

The **Cinquefoils**, members of the genus *Potentilla*, are a large group of mostly perennial plants, with over 75 species in Europe. Their flowers have five petals cupped not only in a calyx of green sepals, but also in an epicalyx—this looks like a second set of sepals beneath the true sepals. Most have yellow flowers, although a few have white or dark red petals. Their fruits are clusters of dry achenes, often partly enclosed by the persistent calyx. Cinquefoils are often confused with buttercups and do resemble those plants, with their yellow flowers and their dark green leaves. But buttercups have simple or divided leaves rather than compound ones with separate leaflets; buttercups lack stipules, whereas members of the rose family have conspicuous stipules; buttercups do not have an epicalyx; and buttercups have a superior ovary while cinquefoils have an inferior one. These last two factors give the flowers of buttercups and cinquefoils quite a different appearance.

Creeping Cinquefoil, *Potentilla reptans* (p. 67), has leaves typical of Five-finger Cinquefoils; there are several species of these, all with leaves that are long-stalked and palmately compound, with several toothed leaflets (often five, hence cinquefoil and five-finger). This one has prostrate stems rooting at the nodes and rosettes of long-stalked leaves. In summer it produces solitary flowers on long stalks, bright yellow with notched petals. This plant is a common sight on roadside verges, in waste places and hedgebanks, less often in grassland, mostly on basic and neutral soils, throughout the British Isles and Europe, except the extreme north.

White Mountain Avens
Dryas octopetala

Water Avens
Geum rivale

Agrimony
Agrimonia eupatoria

Wood Avens
Geum urbanum

Sibbaldia
Sibbaldia procumbens

Salad Burnet
Sanguisorba minor

Great Burnet
Sanguisorba officinalis

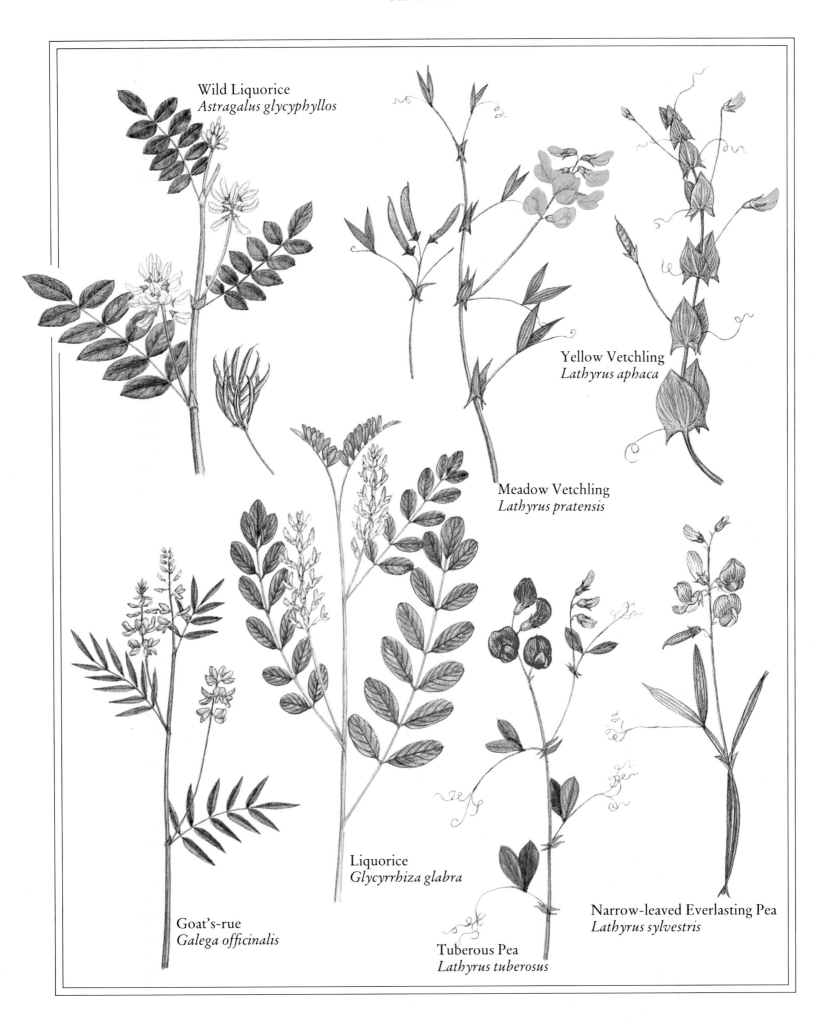

Wild Liquorice
Astragalus glycyphyllos

Yellow Vetchling
Lathyrus aphaca

Meadow Vetchling
Lathyrus pratensis

Liquorice
Glycyrrhiza glabra

Goat's-rue
Galega officinalis

Tuberous Pea
Lathyrus tuberosus

Narrow-leaved Everlasting Pea
Lathyrus sylvestris

racemes of crimson flowers are borne on erect stalks. Its roots bear fleshy, edible tubers. This plant is found in fields and vineyards across much of Europe, except the north and Portugal. It has been introduced into England and southern Scotland, where it is a rare inhabitant of cornfields and hedges; it is sometimes grown in gardens.

Narrow-leaved Everlasting Pea, *Lathyrus sylvestris* (p. 73), has broadly winged stems and a pair of narrow leaflets on each tendrilled leaf. Stems and leaflets look similar. The flowers are rose pink, often tinged with green or purple; they grow in racemes on erect stems and are followed by compressed, brown pods. This plant grows in woods, hedgerows and thickets, scattered across most of Europe and Great Britain. It is most common in southern England and absent from Ireland.

The **Sea Pea**, *Lathyrus japonicus*, is a very local plant, growing on dunes and shingle beaches on the coast of western and northern Europe; in Britain it is found from East Anglia to Cornwall. It has prostrate, angled stems, 3–6 pairs of soft, slightly fleshy, often bluish, elliptical leaflets on each tendrilled leaf, and broadly triangular stipules. In the axils of the leaves grow racemes of flowers on long stalks; they are purple at first, becoming blue as they age.

In **Bitter Vetch**, *Lathyrus montanus*, the tendrils are reduced to fine points at the tips of the leaves. This is an erect, not a scrambling plant, with winged stems up to 50cm (20in) tall, and leaves with 2–4 pairs of linear to elliptical leaflets. It produces loose racemes of crimson flowers on long stalks, the flowers turning blue or green as they age, and followed by hairless, red-brown pods. This perennial plant has swollen, tuberous roots and creeping rhizomes. It grows in hills and mountains, in rough grassland, woods and hedgerows across much of Europe; it is scattered throughout the British Isles, except in East Anglia, more commonly in the west.

There are about 55 *Vicia* species in Europe. Some are crop plants, like *Vicia faba*, the Broad Bean. One subspecies of **Common Vetch**, *V. sativa* subsp. *sativa*, is cultivated for fodder and as a green manure. However, the subspecies *nigra* is a native wild plant, growing in grassy places, fields and hedges throughout Europe and the British Isles. It is an annual, with slender stems and pairs of violet or purple flowers in the axils of the pinnate leaves. Its stipules are often toothed and dark-blotched and its tendrils are branched.

Bush Vetch, *Vicia sepium*, is an almost hairless perennial species, a trailing plant which may take over a large patch of ground with its branched stems, pinnate leaves and hungry tendrils. The stems grow to 1m (3ft) tall and are slender, the leaves have 5–9 pairs of ovate leaflets and a branched tendril at the tip, and the stipules are half arrow-shaped and usually untoothed. The flowers appear in summer in clusters of 2–6 in the leaf axils; they are pale bluish-purple and followed by black, beaked pods. Plants may be found in grassy places, in hedgerows and thickets across Europe and the British Isles.

Yellow Vetch, *Vicia lutea*, is a tufted perennial plant, with branched, often prostrate stems and pinnate leaves. It varies in texture from smooth to hairy, has 3–10 pairs of lance-shaped leaflets on each leaf, together with a branched tendril, and has small, triangular stipules. The flowers appear in summer and are pale yellow, borne on short stalks singly or in small clusters in the leaf axils. Yellow Vetch is a relatively uncommon plant found on cliffs and shingle beaches on the coasts of southern and western Europe, rarely in Great Britain (and then mostly in England). It is also introduced inland in some places.

Tufted Vetch, *Vicia cracca*, also called Cats-peas and Tine-grass, is probably one of the most familiar vetches, growing in meadows and fields, along roadsides and in woods throughout Europe and the British Isles. It is a scrambling plant up to 1m (3ft) tall, with pinnate leaves ending in branched tendrils that twine around anything they contact. In summer it produces showy, one-sided racemes of bright bluish-purple flowers growing on long stalks in the axils of the leaves. They are followed by squarish pods which crack open in hot summer sun to release the seeds.

Wood Vetch, *Vicia sylvatica*, grows in hills and mountains, in rocky woods and bushy places, or by the sea on shingle banks and cliffs. It is scattered throughout most of Europe and Great Britain. This is a hairless perennial plant, scrambling up to 2m (6ft) in height (but often only half this size), with pinnate leaves, branched tendrils and semi-circular, toothed stipules. The flowers appear in summer in loose, one-sided racemes in the leaf axils; they are white with purple veins.

Some of the *Vicia* species are weeds—the tares of the Bible. **Hairy Tare**, *V. hirsuta*, was once a troublesome weed of grain fields, contaminating the harvest so that the flour was unpalatable. It grows throughout Europe and the British Isles in fields and grassy places. This little annual plant is often only 30cm (1ft) tall, with branched, slender stems and very narrow leaflets on its pinnate leaves, scrambling through other plants with branched tendrils. In summer it bears small racemes of purplish or whitish flowers. Smooth Tare, *V. tetrasperma*, is a similar plant found in grassy places. It has only 3–6 pairs of leaflets on each leaf (compared to 4–10 pairs in Hairy Tare) and pale purple flowers borne singly or in pairs.

The **Restharrows**, *Ononis* species, are small shrubs or herbaceous plants. They have simple or clover-like leaves in which the veins end in teeth at the edges of the leaflets, and conspicuous stipules fused to the leaf stalks. There are nearly 50 species in Europe. **Common Restharrow**, *O. repens* (p. 77), is a subshrubby plant, with woody, branched stems, often prostrate and rooting near the base, turning upwards near the tips and growing about 60cm (2ft) tall. Both stems and clover-like leaves are hairy. The plants flower in summer, producing loose, leafy racemes of pinkish-purple flowers in the axils of the leaves. This restharrow grows in rough grassy places, on

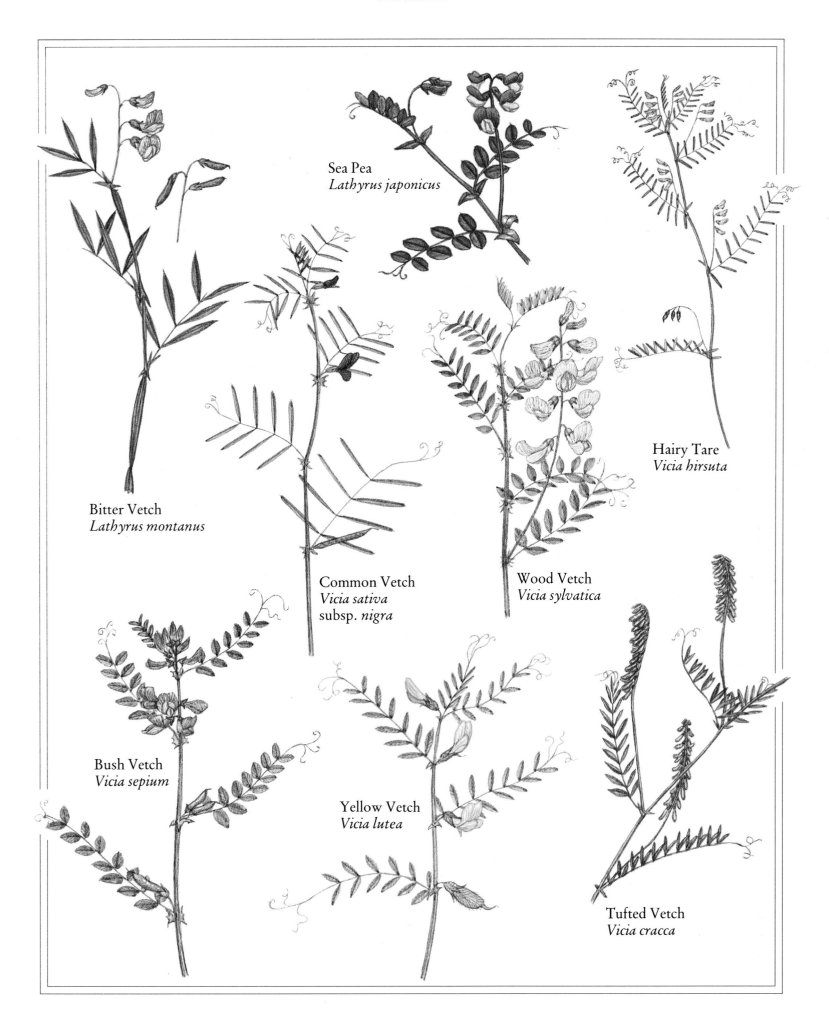

Sea Pea
Lathyrus japonicus

Bitter Vetch
Lathyrus montanus

Common Vetch
Vicia sativa
subsp. *nigra*

Wood Vetch
Vicia sylvatica

Hairy Tare
Vicia hirsuta

Bush Vetch
Vicia sepium

Yellow Vetch
Vicia lutea

Tufted Vetch
Vicia cracca

banks, roadsides and in pastures, on dry calcareous or basic soils across much of Europe, and is scattered throughout the British Isles, becoming rare in western Scotland and Ireland.

Spiny Restharrow, *Ononis spinosa*, is a similar, slightly taller plant, but its stems do not root at the base; instead, they have two lines of hairs rather than hairs all over, and their side shoots end in stiff spines. The leaves have narrow leaflets and the flowers are pink or reddish-purple. This species grows in rough grassy places, on banks, roadsides and pastures on dry calcareous soils throughout Europe. It is scattered across England, becoming rare in Wales and the southwest.

Ribbed Melilot, *Melilotus officinalis*, is a tall biennial plant up to 1.5m (5ft) in height, with many slender racemes of yellow flowers in late summer. It has clover-like leaves with toothed, elliptical leaflets and a scent of coumarin (new-mown hay), especially when drying. It grows beside roadsides, in waste places and fields throughout continental Europe and has been introduced to the British Isles, where it is common in England and eastern Ireland, rare in Wales and Scotland. **Tall Melilot**, *M. altissima*, is often perennial in its growth. It has a similar distribution to Ribbed Melilot. **White Melilot**, *M. alba*, with white flowers, also grows in similar places across Europe and has become naturalized in England.

Several small annual plants in the genus *Medicago*, are found in Europe and the British Isles. **Black Medick**, *M. lupulina*, is a much-branched, trailing, often prostrate plant, sometimes growing 30cm (1ft) tall or more, especially if supported by surrounding vegetation. It has small, clover-like leaves with rounded, often toothed and notched leaflets, and heads of tiny, bright yellow flowers on long stalks in the leaf axils. The plant is easy to distinguish in fruit because its ripe pods resemble tiny, black, coiled, kidney-shaped shells. Black Medick grows in grassy places throughout Europe and the British Isles, becoming more local in Scotland.

Spotted Medick, *Medicago arabica*, is another annual, a sprawling plant with stems growing up to 50cm (20in) tall. Its clover-like leaves have dark blotches in the centre of each leaflet and its larger, yellow flowers are borne in small clusters on long stalks in the leaf axils. The pods form round, spiny spirals. This plant grows in grassy and waste places, especially on sandy soils across most of Europe; in Britain it is confined mostly to southern and eastern England.

Alfalfa or Lucerne, *Medicago sativa*, is a hairy perennial with erect or sprawling stems growing up to 90cm (3ft) tall. It has clover-like leaves and racemes of blue-violet flowers in the leaf axils and terminating the stems. The pods that follow are twisted into a spiral with a hole through the centre. This plant comes originally from Asia, is cultivated as a forage plant in many parts of Europe and has become naturalized in grassy, waste and cultivated places in many countries. In the British Isles it is most likely to be found in England, more locally in Scotland, Wales and Ireland.

Classical Fenugreek, *Trigonella foenum-graecum*, has been used in herb medicine since the times of the ancient Egyptians (and probably before that). Today it is grown as cattle fodder in central and southern Europe and used in veterinary medicine; its seeds are still used in herbal medicine, especially made into a poultice to relieve abscesses and boils, or as a tonic; the seeds are also used in curry. Fenugreek is an erect, annual plant, growing about 50cm (20in) tall. It has many clover-like leaves and solitary or paired, creamy-white flowers in the axils of the uppermost leaves. The pods are narrow and sickle-like. This plant comes from Asia; it has been introduced to much of Europe but is absent from the north and from the British Isles. Several other *Trigonella* species grow wild in Europe, including Star-fruited Fenugreek, *T. monspeliaca*. It is a small annual with clover-like leaves and yellow flowers found in waste places across much of Europe, except the north.

Bird's-foot Fenugreek, *Trifolium ornithopodioides* (p. 79), was at one time placed in the genus *Trigonella* with Classical Fenugreek, but modern botanists think it more closely related to the clovers. It is a branched, little annual plant growing 20cm (8in) tall at most, with slender stems and clover-like leaves, each with three oval, serrated leaflets. In summer it produces small clusters of 2–4 pinkish-white flowers on long stalks in the leaf axils, followed by curved pods. This plant grows in dry, sandy and gravelly places, often near the coast in short grassland, in scattered localities around western and southern Europe, England, Wales and eastern Ireland.

Clovers are more familiar members of the genus *Trifolium*. White Clover, with its creeping stems, white-banded leaflets and heads of white flowers is known to everyone who has played in grass as a child; or to anyone who has searched for the proverbial lucky leaf with four leaflets instead of three. Red Clover is almost as familiar, with its much bigger clumps of leafy stems and large red flower heads, on roadsides and rough grassland. There are nearly 300 *Trifolium* species, mostly found in north temperate regions, with about 100 in Europe. Several are grown as fodder or forage crops.

Clovers are, in general, distinguishable from other leguminous plants by their leaves with three leaflets, their stipules joined to the leaf stalks, and particularly by their heads or dense head-like spikes of flowers. Their flowers are rich in nectar and much sought out by bees, both hive bees and bumble bees. Honey made from clover nectar is one of the best kinds. The petals, and often the sepals, persist on the flower heads when the pods are formed, so that the whole thing looks like a brown, withered parody of its former self.

White Clover, *Trifolium repens* (p. 79), is the one found most often in lawns. Often unwanted, it is actually useful, since the presence of its roots, with their nodules, improves the soil; it is often grown as a forage plant. In the wild it grows in all kinds of grassy places, usually on heavy soils, throughout Europe and the British Isles. This is a creeping species with

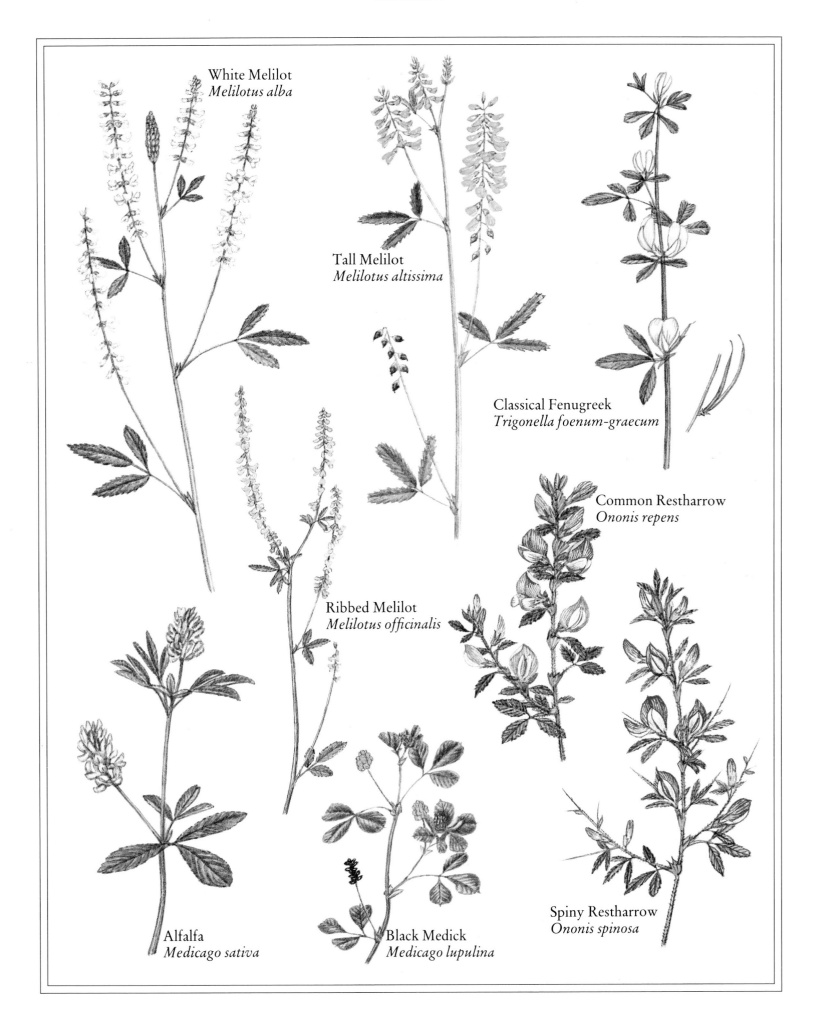

White Melilot
Melilotus alba

Tall Melilot
Melilotus altissima

Classical Fenugreek
Trigonella foenum-graecum

Common Restharrow
Ononis repens

Ribbed Melilot
Melilotus officinalis

Alfalfa
Medicago sativa

Black Medick
Medicago lupulina

Spiny Restharrow
Ononis spinosa

Marsh Mallow
Althaea officinalis

Hollyhock
Alcea rosea

Small Tree Mallow
Lavatera cretica

Tree Mallow
Lavatera arborea

Musk Mallow
Malva moschata

Common Mallow
Malva sylvestris

Dwarf Mallow
Malva neglecta

Flower-of-an-hour
Hibiscus trionum

tic coasts of Europe north to the south and west coasts of England and Wales, and on the south coast of Ireland. If found elsewhere it is likely to have been introduced.

Small Tree Mallow, *Lavatera cretica* (p. 91), is a smaller annual or biennial plant with herbaceous stems, lobed leaves and lilac flowers with widely separated petals. It grows in waste places near the sea on the Mediterranean and west coasts of Europe, north to Cornwall, the Scilly Isles and Jersey.

Hibiscus is a large genus, with about 200 species of shrubs and herbs from the warmer regions of the world. **Flower-of-an-hour**, *H. trionum* (p. 91), comes from southeastern Europe but is grown in France, Spain and Portugal. It is an annual, with an erect, branched stem up to 60cm (2ft) tall and three-lobed, wavy-margined leaves. Solitary flowers grow in the leaf axils in summer; they are quite large, pale yellow with purple centres and last for only a few hours. The fruits are hairy capsules divided into five sections, each enclosed in the bristly, five-angled calyx which becomes inflated and papery.

Violet family
Violaceae

For many people this family is synonymous with the pansies and violets, *Viola* species, although there are actually 22 genera and 900 species in the family, and only 500 of them are in the genus *Viola*. They are found in temperate and tropical regions, and are mostly herbaceous plants.

Family features The flowers are solitary or borne in racemes; they are regular or bilaterally symmetrical. Each has five persistent, overlapping sepals and five petals; these are usually unequal and the lowermost is spurred. There are five stamens, the lower two often spurred at the base and with the anthers of all five joined around the ovary. The ovary is superior with one cell. The fruits are capsules or berries. The leaves are simple and alternate with leafy stipules.

There are over 90 *Viola* species in Europe. Many appear to flower only in spring, but actually bloom through spring and summer, producing two kinds of flowers. The familiar ones, with bright petals, are spring flowers; summer flowers remain hidden beneath the foliage, do not open and are self-pollinated. It is these that form most of the seed. Violet flowers are quite distinctive, with five petals forming a bilaterally symmetrical and spurred flower. They come in variations on three colours (blue-violet, yellow and white), are often veined and the two lateral petals are often bearded near the base. Plants may form rosettes of leaves with flowers on separate stalks or may have long, leafy stems with flowers in the leaf axils.

Sweet Violet, *Viola odorata*, is a small perennial plant only 20cm (8in) tall, with rosettes of long-stalked, broadly heart-shaped leaves and long, leafless runners which root and pro-

duce new plants. In spring sweet-scented, deep purple or white flowers grow from the crown of the plant; closed flowers are produced throughout the summer, never appearing above the leaves. Sweet Violets grow in hedgerows, coppiced woodland, thickets and plantations, usually on calcareous soils, throughout Europe, in England, Wales and central Ireland. They are also grown in gardens, valued for their perfume and used in herb medicine, in remedies for coughs and colds and in headache treatments. Hairy Violet, *V. hirta*, is similar but lacks runners, has narrower leaves and scentless, paler blue-violet flowers. It grows in calcareous grassland and scrub throughout most of Europe, mostly in England in the British Isles.

Common Dog-violet, *Viola riviniana*, is probably the most familiar violet for many people, abundant throughout Europe and the British Isles, found in open woods and hedgerows, heaths and pastures. It is a little perennial plant, often only 15cm (6in) tall, with a central clump of long-stalked, heart-shaped leaves. The spring flowers grow on separate stems, each one in the axil of a long-stalked leaf; they are blue-violet with a paler, often whitish spur. Closed flowers appear in summer.

Heath Dog-violet, *Viola canina*, has no central leaf rosette; instead the leaves all grow on sprawling stems and the plant may reach 30cm (1ft) tall. The leaves are ovate to somewhat triangular in shape, borne on long stalks, and the spring flowers are blue with a yellowish spur. This is a very variable species found scattered throughout Europe and the British Isles, in dry grassland and heaths, sand-dunes and open woods, also in fens, often on acid soils.

Marsh Violet, *Viola palustris*, has long, slender rhizomes with leaves growing from the nodes; these have broad, almost kidney-shaped blades and long stalks. The spring flowers are borne singly on long stalks; they are lilac with darker veins. This little plant grows in marshes and wet heaths, fens and bogs, in acid soils across much of Europe and the British Isles (but is absent from much of the Midlands and East Anglia).

Yellow Wood Violet, *Viola biflora*, grows in the mountains of western Europe, in damp, shady woods or among rocks; it is not found in the British Isles. It is a delicate plant, with slender, leafy stems bearing kidney-shaped leaves on long stalks and pairs of golden-yellow flowers veined with brown.

Pansies do not produce closed flowers in summer; instead they go on producing showy flowers for a much longer period than violets. **Wild Pansy** or Heartsease, *Viola tricolor*, is one of the plants from which Garden Pansies are derived, with much smaller flowers than its offspring, but the same sprawling, leafy stems. It has two subspecies. Subsp. *tricolor* is found in cultivated ground and waste places across most of Europe and the British Isles; it is an annual with blue-violet flowers. Subsp. *curtisii* grows on dunes and in grassy places near the sea around much of the British and Irish coastline, and on the coasts of the North and Baltic Seas. It is a perennial plant and may have blue-violet, yellow, or multicoloured flowers.

Sweet Violet
Viola odorata

Field Pansy
Viola arvensis

Mountain Pansy
Viola lutea

Marsh Violet
Viola palustris

Wild Pansy
Viola tricolor

Yellow Wood Violet
Viola biflora

Heath Dog-violet
Viola canina

Common Dog-violet
Viola riviniana

Mountain Pansy, *Viola lutea* (p. 93), is the other ancestor of Garden Pansies, the cross between the two species resulting in the large hybrid varieties. Mountain Pansy is a perennial, with creeping rhizomes and sprawling stems. The lowermost leaves are ovate, but upper ones are much divided and so are their stipules. The flowers are coloured in combinations of blue-violet, red and yellow, but the lowest petal is always yellow at the base. This plant grows in hills, in short grassland and among rocks, often on base-rich soils; it grows throughout much of western and central Europe, in north Wales, northern England and Scotland, and a few places in Ireland.

Field Pansy, *Viola arvensis* (p. 93), has sprawling, branched, leafy stems, and small, creamy-white flowers, often with blue-tinged upper petals. It grows in waste places and may become a weed in cultivated land, usually in neutral or basic soils, throughout Europe and the British Isles.

Daphne family
Thymelaeaceae

A family of about 50 genera and 500 species of trees and shrubs (rarely herbs), found throughout most of the world.

There are about 70 *Daphne* species in the temperate regions of the world, several grown in gardens for their fragrant flowers. About 17 are found in Europe. **Mezereon**, *D. mezereum*, is a deciduous shrub about 1m (3ft) tall, with a few erect branches and smooth, light green, lance-shaped leaves. The flowers are pinkish-purple, sweetly scented and appear before the leaves in early spring. They are characteristic of *Daphne* flowers in having a corolla-like calyx-tube enclosing the cylindrical receptacle and no petals. Very poisonous 'berries' follow the flowers, ripening bright red in autumn; they may be mistaken for redcurrants with fatal results. The fruits are technically drupes since they have one seed rather than many. This plant grows in woods and scrub on calcareous soils, but is becoming less common all the time due to overcollecting and changes in land management. It is, or was, found across most of Europe, and can still be found in some places in England.

Spurge-laurel, *Daphne laureola*, is an evergreen shrub, also with a few erect branches, growing about 1m (3ft) tall. The leaves are leathery and glossy dark green, ovate to lance-shaped and crowded towards the tops of the branches on the young green shoots. The flowers appear in spring, little clusters of scented, green bells in the axils of the leaves; they are followed by deadly poisonous black berries in the autumn. In fact, the whole plant is poisonous, like many *Daphne* species. Spurge-laurel grows in woods, usually on calcareous soils, locally throughout much of Europe, except the north and Portugal. It is local but widespread in England and Wales, not found in Ireland or Scotland, unless introduced.

Annual Thymelaea, *Thymelaea passerina*, is unusual among members of this family, in being an annual herbaceous plant. It grows 20–50cm (8–20in) tall, has erect, rigid stems with pointed, narrow leaves and tiny greenish flowers in the leaf axils. It grows in dry waste places across much of continental Europe, except the north. It is absent from the British Isles.

Oleaster family
Elaeagnaceae

A family of trees and shrubs , with only 3 genera and about 50 species, found in northern temperate and subtropical areas of the world. Several species of *Elaeagnus* are grown in gardens.

Sea-buckthorn, *Hippophaë rhamnoides*, is a branched, spiny shrub, its old stems brown, its young twigs and narrow grey leaves covered with silvery scales. The leaves are crowded on to lateral shoots, expanding after the flowers appear in spring. Male and female flowers grow in small clusters on separate plants; they are petal-less, tiny and greenish, and the female flowers are followed in autumn by bright orange, poisonous berries. Sea-buckthorn forms thickets up to 3m (9ft) tall, with many suckers, on fixed dunes, sometimes on cliffs, on the Atlantic and Baltic coasts of Europe, and around the coast of Great Britain. It has been introduced to Ireland and also grows on shingle banks in the rivers of central Europe.

Rockrose family
Cistaceae

There are about 8 genera and 200 species in this small family of herbs and shrubs, the majority found in the Mediterranean region. Some, like the *Cistus* species, are grown in gardens.

Family features The flowers are hermaphrodite and regular, with three or five contorted free sepals, five often contorted, overlapping petals which soon fall, many free stamens and a superior ovary with one, three or five cells. The fruits are capsules. The leaves are usually opposite and simple and the plants often have star-shaped hairs.

Common Rockrose, *Helianthemum nummularium*, is a small shrub with sprawling, often rooting stems 30cm (1ft) tall at most and often prostrate. The stems bear opposite pairs of leaves, green above with dense white hairs beneath, and produce a succession of bright yellow flowers in summer. This plant grows in dry, basic grassland, often among rocks or on banks, throughout Europe and most of Great Britain; it is absent from Cornwall and northwest Scotland, very rare in Ireland. Many varieties are grown in rock gardens. **White Rockrose**, *H. apenninum*, is a similar plant but has white

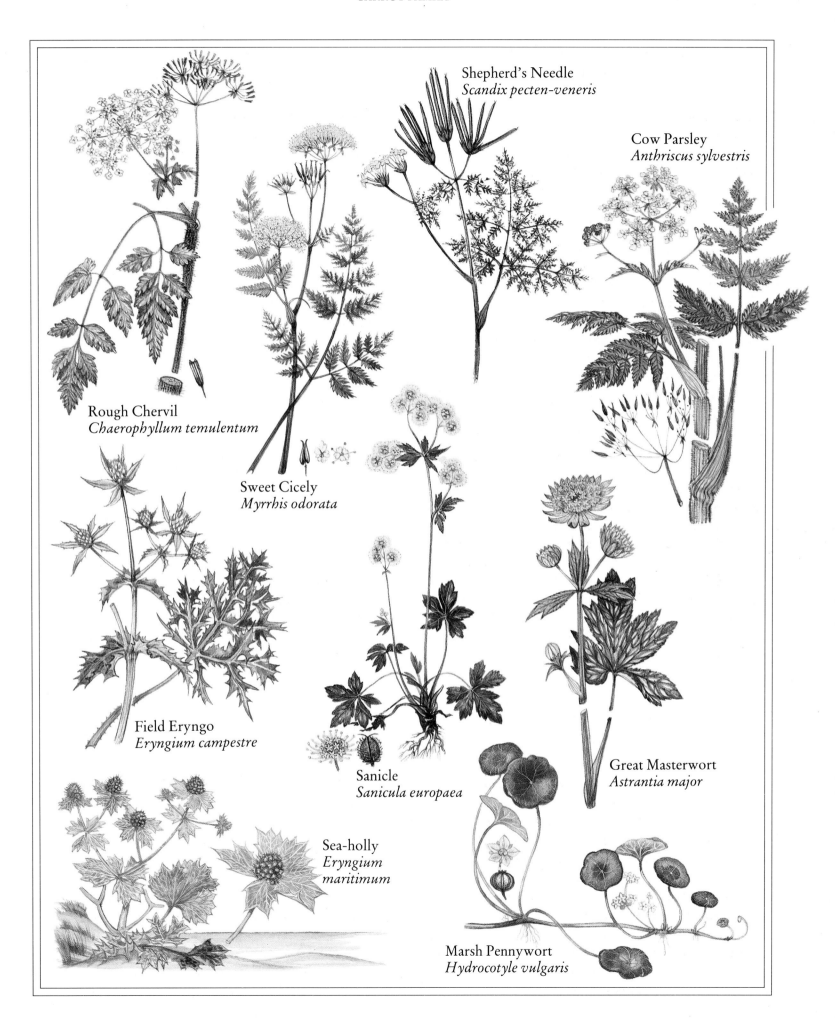

Shepherd's Needle
Scandix pecten-veneris

Cow Parsley
Anthriscus sylvestris

Rough Chervil
Chaerophyllum temulentum

Sweet Cicely
Myrrhis odorata

Field Eryngo
Eryngium campestre

Sanicle
Sanicula europaea

Great Masterwort
Astrantia major

Sea-holly
Eryngium maritimum

Marsh Pennywort
Hydrocotyle vulgaris

103

Sea-holly, *Eryngium maritimum* (p. 103), is not immediately recognizable as an umbellifer; its flowers are borne in heads rather than umbels and its leathery leaves are spiny, like those of thistles, with white veins and a thickened white margin. This stiff perennial plant is blue-grey in colour, with a clump of three-lobed, spine-edged basal leaves and branched flowering stems up to 60cm (2ft) tall in late summer; these have palmately lobed, also spiny leaves. The metallic blue flower heads are borne in clusters terminating the stems, cupped in spiny bracts. This plant is not very popular with holiday-makers; it grows on sandy beaches, sand-dunes and shingle banks around the coasts of the British Isles and western Europe, north to southern Scandinavia. It can be grown in gardens and the flower heads dried for flower arrangements.

Field Eryngo, *Eryngium campestre* (p. 103), is a less prickly species, a perennial with a clump of pinnate basal leaves on long stalks and erect flowering stems growing up to 60cm (2ft) tall. These are well endowed with spiny leaves, their bases clasping the stem, and with a terminal, branched inflorescence of many pale green, egg-shaped flower heads. Each head is cupped in several narrow, spine-edged bracts. This plant grows in dry, grassy places throughout much of Europe, except the north. In Britain it is not common, found only at a few scattered sites in southern England.

Rough Chervil, *Chaerophyllum temulentum* (p. 103), is a much more typical member of the Carrot family, as are the rest of the plants included here. It is a biennial, with a clump of twice- or three-times pinnate leaves in the first year and leafy flowering stems up to 1m (3ft) tall, with compound umbels of white flowers, in the second. The stems are solid, stiffly hairy and purple spotted; the leaves are also hairy and turn from dark green to purple as they age. The umbels are nodding when the flowers are in bud, each one has several narrow bracts beneath and 8–10 slender rays. This plant is found in most of Europe and much of the British Isles; it is absent from western Ireland and north and west Scotland. It is one of several umbellifers found in hedgebanks, flowering in sequence throughout the summer; this one is the second, coming into bloom just after Cow Parsley, from which it can be distinguished by its purple-spotted stems. It is poisonous, causing dizziness.

Cow Parsley, *Anthriscus sylvestris* (p. 103), is the first of the common hedgebank umbellifers to flower, blooming in early summer with a froth of lacy flowers (its other name is Queen Anne's Lace). It is another biennial plant, with twice- to three-times pinnate leaves in the first year and leafy, furrowed flowering stems in the second. They grow up to 1m (3ft) tall and bear many compound umbels of white flowers. Each umbel has 6–12 rays, 4–6 narrow bracts and an outer ring of flowers in which the outside petals are larger than the others. The fruits are black and bristly. This plant is often abundant in woodland margins and hedges, or in waste places throughout most of the British Isles and Europe.

Bur Chervil, *Anthriscus caucalis*, is a related annual plant, with hollow stems, twice- or three-times pinnate leaves and small umbels of white flowers in early summer. Its fruits are distinctive—covered in hooked bristles like small burs. It grows in hedgebanks and waste places scattered throughout much of the British Isles, especially near the sea but not in the north and west, throughout Europe, except the north.

Shepherd's Needle, *Scandix pecten-veneris* (p. 103), was a common weed at one time, found in arable land throughout Europe, including southeastern England. However, it is now rather rare as a result of the use of modern weed-killers, together with techniques for producing cleaner seed. It is a winter annual, a more or less hairless plant, with an erect branched stem up to 60cm (2ft tall) and two- to three-times pinnate, ferny leaves. The small white flowers are borne in simple umbels, usually growing in pairs in early summer. The plant becomes highly distinctive when the fruits form, for they are 15–80mm ($\frac{1}{2}$–3in) long with extremely long beaks. This plant has many names, as it has been familiar to farm workers for centuries; the names mostly describe the fruits, for they form at harvest time when the men were in the fields gathering the wheat. Folk names range from Venus' Comb and Ladies' Comb, to Darning Needles, Adam's Needles and even Devil's Needles.

Sweet Cicely, *Myrrhis odorata* (p. 103), is one of the edible members of this family; its leaves and fruits taste of aniseed and can be added to salads or used as a sweetener. The young roots can be eaten as a vegetable. This is a perennial plant, with hollow, rather grooved stems growing up to 2m (6ft) tall and twice- or three-times pinnate leaves with serrated segments. It blooms in early summer, with compound umbels of white flowers, some umbels with hermaphrodite flowers, others with male flowers only and these with shorter, more slender rays. The outer flowers of the umbels have unequal petals. The ripe fruits are shiny brown, oblong and deeply ridged with bristly hairs on the ridges. Plants grow in grassy places, hedges and woods, hills and mountains across Europe, in Wales, northern England, northern Ireland and Scotland.

Alexanders, *Smyrnium olusatrum*, is a mainly maritime plant found on coastal cliffs, but also in waste places, woods and hedgebanks, both near the sea and less often inland. It comes originally from the Mediterranean region, but has become naturalized northwards to France, Holland and the British Isles (rarely in Scotland). At one time it was cultivated and eaten as a vegetable, but has been replaced by celery. This is a stout biennial plant, its second-year stems growing up to 1.5m (5ft) tall; they are solid when young, becoming hollow with age and furrowed, branched near the top to produce dense, rounded umbels of yellow-green flowers in early summer. Each compound umbel has 7–15 rays. The leaves are dark green and shiny, basal ones up to 30cm (1ft) long and three-times divided into three leaflets; all the leaves have broadly sheathing bases.

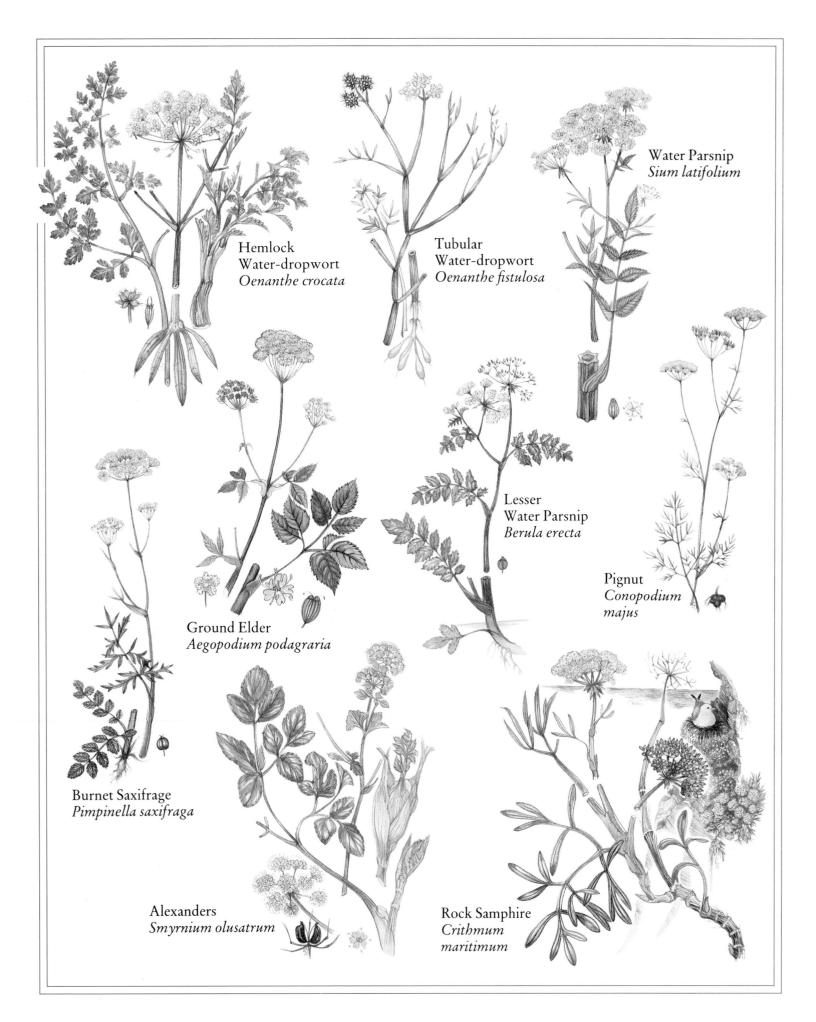

Hemlock
Water-dropwort
Oenanthe crocata

Tubular
Water-dropwort
Oenanthe fistulosa

Water Parsnip
Sium latifolium

Lesser
Water Parsnip
Berula erecta

Pignut
*Conopodium
majus*

Ground Elder
Aegopodium podagraria

Burnet Saxifrage
Pimpinella saxifraga

Alexanders
Smyrnium olusatrum

Rock Samphire
*Crithmum
maritimum*

Pignut or Earthnut, *Conopodium majus* (p. 105), is a slender plant, a perennial growing in woods and fields on acid soils throughout the British Isles and western Europe, north to Norway. It grows from a dark brown, irregular tuber (edible and with a nutty taste), producing broad, twice-pinnate basal leaves which soon wither, and sending up a slender stem about 50cm (20in) tall, its upper leaves finely divided with linear segments. It flowers in early summer, producing a few compound umbels with 6–12 rays; each is nodding in bud and opens into white flowers, unequal on the outside.

Burnet Saxifrage, *Pimpinella saxifraga* (p. 105), is another relatively slender perennial plant, this one found in dry, grassy places, often on calcareous soils, scattered throughout the British Isles and across most of Europe. It has an erect stem, rough in texture and solid, with pinnate leaves and serrated leaflets, the lower leaves twice-pinnate. It blooms in late summer, producing flat-topped, compound umbels with 10–22 rays and white flowers. At one time this plant was used in herb medicine, mainly to soothe coughs and bronchitis. Its less common relative, Greater Burnet Saxifrage, *P. major*, was used in the same way. It is a larger plant with hollow, angled stems, once-pinnate leaves and white or pinkish flowers. It grows in grassy places in hedges and woodland edges in England and Ireland, and across much of Europe.

Ground Elder, *Aegopodium podagraria* (p. 105), was used as a medicinal herb at one time to treat gout and rheumatism (hence its other name of Goutweed). It was also grown in gardens for its leaves, which were eaten like spinach; since it spreads into what are often ineradicable colonies with its creeping rhizomes, many owners of old gardens regret this practice. The plant sends up carpets of pinnate leaves in spring and flowering stems in summer. These bear dense, rounded umbels of white flowers, with 10–20 rays in each umbel. It is found throughout the British Isles and most of Europe.

Rock Samphire, *Crithmum maritimum* (p. 105), is a coastal plant, most often growing on cliffs and rocks around the Atlantic and Mediterranean coasts of Europe, around Ireland, on the west coast of Britain from northern England southwards, and on the south coast to East Anglia. It is a branched, perennial, blue-grey plant, with solid, narrowly ridged stems and fleshy, pinnate leaves with narrow leaflets. Yellow-green flowers appear after midsummer, borne in stout umbels with 8–36 rays. Young leaves and stems can be gathered in spring and pickled; young seed pods can be pickled later in the year.

Water Parsnip, *Sium latifolium* (p. 105), is one of several umbellifers found in wet places, growing in fens and marshes across Europe; in Britain it is found in England, mainly in the east, and in central Ireland but is declining in numbers with improved techniques of drainage in farming. This is a perennial plant, with a grooved, hollow stem up to 2m (6ft) tall, twice- or three-times pinnate submerged leaves with linear segments, and aerial pinnate leaves with 9–17 leaflets. The flowers are white, borne in dense, flat-topped umbels with 20–30 rays and large, leaf-like bracts. They appear in late summer.

Lesser Water Parsnip, *Berula erecta* (p. 105), is a similar plant, but it has sprawling stems which root where they touch the ground or the mud beneath the water. This is another semi-aquatic plant, growing in ditches and canals, marshes and ponds across much of Europe and lowland areas of the British Isles; it is rare in Wales and Scotland. It has hollow, narrowly ridged stems, pinnate leaves with serrated leaflets and umbels of white flowers opposite the leaves in late summer. The umbels are rather irregular, with 7–18 rays and leaf-like, often three-lobed bracts. The fruits are more or less globular.

The risk in eating wild umbellifers or using them in herb medicine is that some of the most poisonous of all flowering plants belong to this family and several resemble the useful species. Accurate identification of the family members is thus essential for anyone tempted to use them.

The **Water-dropworts** are a group of about 35 species in the genus *Oenanthe*, found in the north temperate regions of the world, with 13 in Europe. They are hairless perennials, all aquatic or marsh plants, and some are poisonous. **Hemlock Water-dropwort**, *O. crocata* (p. 105), is one of the most deadly umbellifers; its stems may be eaten in mistake for celery and the tuberous roots for parsnips. Death follows rapidly, but poisoning is more common in livestock than in humans. This plant grows in acid soils in wet, grassy places, on woodland edges, in ditches and beside water in western Europe, mostly in the south and west, and in Ireland. Its erect stems are hollow and grooved, up to 1.5m (5ft) tall and its leaves are large—30cm (1ft) long and ferny in appearance, three- to four-times pinnate, with serrated leaflets and sheathing bases to the leaf stalks. Plants flower around midsummer, bearing large, terminal umbels with 10–40 rays and white flowers.

Tubular Water-dropwort, *Oenanthe fistulosa* (p. 105), is also poisonous, although less so. It has erect, hollow stems, 30–90cm (1–3ft) tall, constricted at the nodes and rooting at the lower nodes. The stems grow from a clump of swollen, spindle-shaped roots. The leaves are pinnate with tubular leaf stalks and linear leaflets, and the white flowers are borne in late summer in dense umbels with 2–4 rays. The partial umbels become globular in fruit, with cylindrical fruits. This plant grows in marshes and shallow water across most of Europe; in the British Isles it is found mainly in the east, less commonly in Ireland, rarely in Scotland. Fine-leaved Water-dropwort, *O. aquatica*, is another poisonous species, found in slow-moving or still waters in England, eastern Wales and central Ireland, and across most of Europe. It has submerged leaves with thread-like segments, and three- to four-times pinnate, aerial leaves. Its white flowers grow in umbels opposite the leaves and terminating the stems; each has 4–16 rays.

Fool's Parsley, *Aethusa cynapium*, is another poisonous umbellifer, its chief danger that it may be mistaken for Parsley,

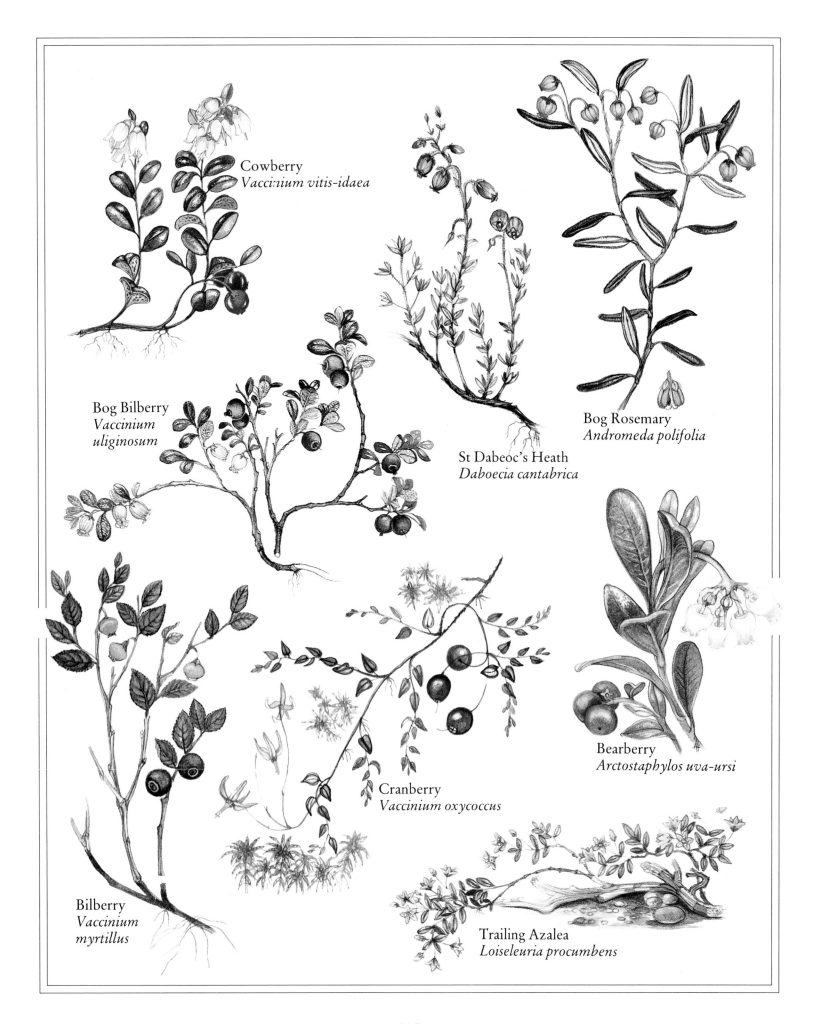

Cowberry
Vaccinium vitis-idaea

Bog Bilberry
Vaccinium uliginosum

St Dabeoc's Heath
Daboecia cantabrica

Bog Rosemary
Andromeda polifolia

Bearberry
Arctostaphylos uva-ursi

Cranberry
Vaccinium oxycoccus

Bilberry
Vaccinium myrtillus

Trailing Azalea
Loiseleuria procumbens

summer this rather dowdy shrub is transformed by the small, bell-like flowers borne along the tops of the stems and along the side shoots; the flowers are pale pinkish-purple, the colour coming from both calyx and corolla. At one time Heather was used for fuel and bedding, as animal fodder and for making brushes and baskets. Heather honey is one of the finest.

Many other heathers or heaths belong to the genus *Erica*, with about 17 species in Europe. This is, however, only a small percentage of the world total of 500, the majority of which are found in South Africa. All the *Erica* species are evergreen shrubs, with small, entire leaves in whorls and bell-shaped or urn-shaped flowers. Their fruits are dry capsules.

Bell-heather, *Erica cinerea*, is one of the most attractive and widespread species, found on dry heaths and moors throughout the British Isles and western Europe, north to Norway. It is a branched shrub about 60cm (2ft) tall, with many upward-growing stems and numerous leafy side shoots; the leaves are linear with inrolled margins, dark green and hairless, borne in whorls of three. In late summer the plants flower, transforming the moors (with Heather) into purple instead of dark green. The flowers are reddish-purple, urn-shaped and constricted at the mouth, borne along the tops of the stems.

Cross-leaved Heath, *Erica tetralix*, is also widespread, found in wetter heaths and moors, also in bogs and pinewoods throughout the British Isles but less commonly in parts of central and southern England than elsewhere. It is also found in western and northern Europe. It is another much-branched shrub about 60cm (2ft) tall, with more or less upright stems. These bear many linear leaves with margins inrolled almost to the midrib, hairy when young and arranged in cross-like whorls of four (hence Cross-leaved Heath). The flowers appear in late summer in little umbel-like clusters nodding at the tops of the stems; they are rose-pink in colour and urn-shaped with a constricted mouth.

Other European heathers are much more restricted in their distributions. **Dorset Heath**, *Erica ciliaris*, grows locally in heathland in Dorset, south Devon and Cornwall in England, also in Connemara in Ireland, and in France, Spain and Portugal. It is not unlike Bell-heather, a small shrub up to 60cm (2ft) tall, with more or less erect branches and leaves in whorls of three on side shoots. The leaves have inrolled margins and a white underside. The flowers are bright pink, urn-shaped and slightly curved above, slightly swollen beneath; they are borne in one-sided racemes at the tops of the stems in summer.

Cornish Heath, *Erica vagans*, is found only on heathland around the Lizard in Cornwall, in Fermanagh in Ireland and in parts of France and northern Spain. It grows up to 80cm (30in) tall, and has erect branches with no side shoots. The leaves are linear with inrolled margins, and borne four or five in a whorl. The flowers are small and bell-shaped, pale lilac with purple-brown anthers protruding from the mouth, borne in dense, leafy racemes at the tops of the stems in late summer.

Irish Heath, *Erica erigena*, grows in bogs and wet heaths in Galway and Mayo in Ireland, also from western France to Spain and Portugal. This is a larger shrub, up to 2m (6ft) tall, with many more or less upright branches without side shoots. It has dark green linear leaves with inrolled margins, borne four in a whorl. The flowers are tubular and dull pinkish-purple, with dark purple anthers half-protruding; they are borne in one-sided racemes at the tops of the stems.

Crowberry family
Empetraceae

A very small family, with 3 genera and 9 species, found in north temperate and Arctic regions, southern South America and the island of Tristan da Cunha. They are evergreen shrubs resembling the heathers.

Crowberry, *Empetrum nigrum* (p. 119), is the only widespread or common member of the family in Europe. It is a low-growing shrub with numerous erect and sprawling stems forming low mounds, the stems becoming prostrate and rooting at the edges of the mounds. The stems are densely covered with small, leathery, needle-like leaves alternately arranged. The leaves have strongly inrolled margins to reduce water loss. Tiny pink flowers grow in the axils of the leaves, male and female flowers on separate plants, and the female plants go on to produce juicy black berries. Crowberry grows in peaty soils on moors and the drier parts of bogs, in birch and pine woods in Ireland, Scotland, Wales and northern England, becoming rare in the Midlands and south. It is also found in suitable habitats across much of Europe. Mountain Crowberry is a subspecies of this plant, subsp. *hermaphroditum*, found at higher altitudes; its stems do not root at the edges of the mounds and its flowers are hermaphrodite.

Diapensia family
Diapensiaceae

A very small family, with 6 genera and about 20 species of evergreen herbs or dwarf shrubs, found in the north temperate and Arctic regions of the world. Some are beautiful plants grown in gardens. They are related to the heathers.

Diapensia, *Diapensia lapponica* (p. 119), is an evergreen cushion-like plant, with branched stems and crowded, overlapping leaves. In spring white, bell-shaped flowers (with their parts in fives) appear on short, erect branches all over the mat. This is a far northern plant, growing in rocky places in the Arctic mountains and tundra. It is found in two places in the Scottish mountains, on exposed ridges in Inverness.

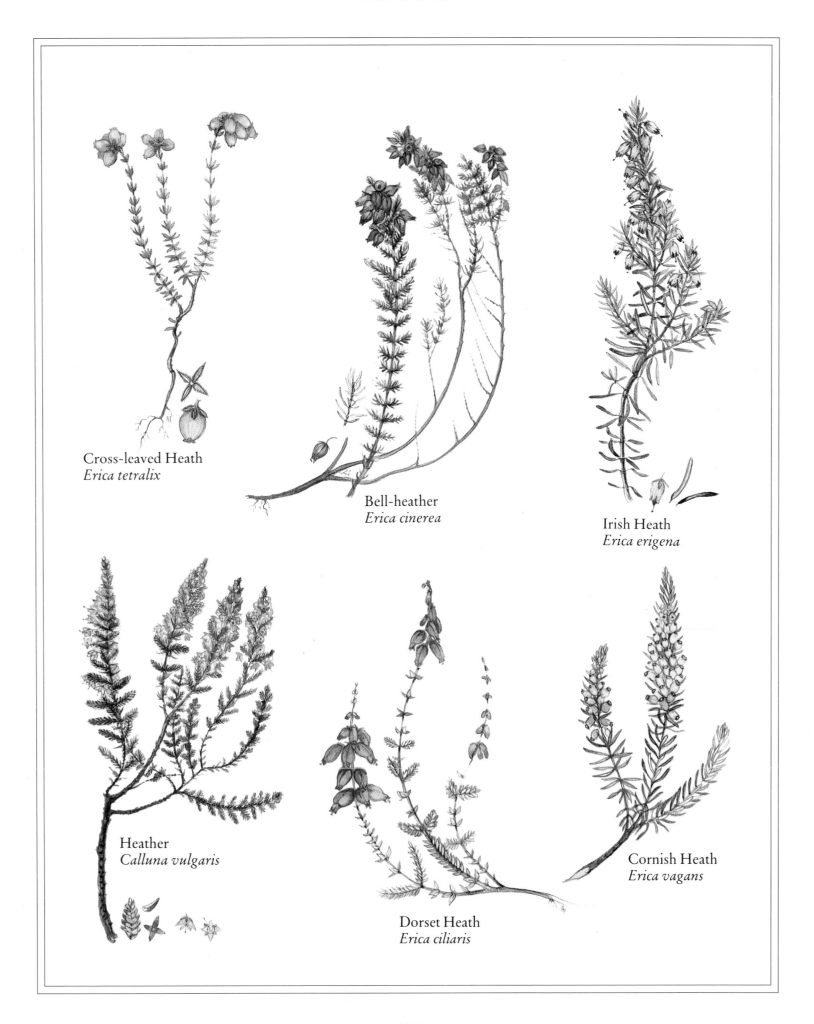

Cross-leaved Heath
Erica tetralix

Bell-heather
Erica cinerea

Irish Heath
Erica erigena

Heather
Calluna vulgaris

Dorset Heath
Erica ciliaris

Cornish Heath
Erica vagans

Wintergreen family
Pyrolaceae

A small family with 4 genera and about 40 species of evergreen herbs, mostly found in Arctic and northern temperate regions, sometimes included in the Ericaceae, the Heath family. All the species are partially saprophytic and associated with raw humus, often growing in pine woods.

Family features The flowers are solitary or borne in clusters, often nodding, white, pink or purple. They are regular and hermaphrodite, each one with four or five sepals fused to form a calyx, and five free petals. There are 10 stamens and the ovary is superior with five cells. The fruit is a globular capsule with many small seeds. The leaves are simple, in basal rosettes or, if on the stems, alternate or in whorls; they lack stipules.

The **Wintergreens**, *Pyrola* species, have creeping rhizomes from which grow rosettes of evergreen leaves and erect, leafless flowering stalks with terminal racemes of nodding flowers. There are about five in Europe. **Small Wintergreen**, *P. minor*, is typical, with broadly elliptical leaves and pinkish-white flowers. It grows in woods, on damp moors and on damp ledges, usually in mountain areas and on calcareous soils, scattered throughout Europe, northern England and Scotland; it is also found more rarely in southern England and Ireland.

Nodding Wintergreen, *Orthilia secunda*, is a similar plant with creeping rhizomes and tufts of light green, ovate leaves on long stalks. However, its nodding, greenish-white flowers grow in one-sided racemes on their erect stalks. This little plant grows in woods and on damp, rocky ledges in the mountains of Scotland and the Scottish islands, in a few places in northern England, Wales and Ireland. It is also found in mountain woods across much of Europe.

One-flowered Wintergreen, *Moneses uniflora*, is a small creeping plant forming rosettes of opposite, long-stalked leaves with ovate blades. In summer the flowers appear, borne singly at the tops of stems only 15cm (6in) tall at most. The flowers are white and sweetly scented, bowl-shaped with a broad base accommodating the 10 stamens and spreading petals. This plant grows in damp mountain woods, usually in coniferous woods on acid soils, in many parts of northern Europe but is quite uncommon; in Britain it is a rare plant found in Scotland.

Bird's-nest family
Monotropaceae

These are specialized plants, lacking chlorophyll and feeding as saprophytes, growing in soils rich in raw humus, often in coniferous woods. They are white, pink or brownish in colour, with a mass of roots covered in mycorrhizal fungi. The fungi presumably enable them to absorb their nutrients from the humus in the soil. These plants are often included in the Wintergreen family and have similar family features other than their totally saprophytic lifestyle. There are about 12 genera and 30 species in the north temperate regions.

Yellow Bird's-nest, *Monotropa hypopitys*, is a distinctive, waxy-looking plant, only 30cm (1ft) tall at most with a clump of fleshy stems covered with alternating, yellowish or ivory-white scale leaves, especially near the base. Each stem is bent over at the top when the flowers are in bud, gradually straightening as the flowers open and are pollinated, so that the capsules are held erect. The flowers are like tubular, yellowish bells, opening in the latter half of summer. This plant is widespread in Europe, occurring locally in England in the British Isles, rarely in Wales and Ireland. It grows in beech and pine woods, and on sand-dunes on the coast.

Primrose family
Primulaceae

There are about 20 genera and 1000 species of herbs in this family, mostly found in the northern hemisphere. They include some choice garden plants: primroses and polyanthus, cyclamens for the greenhouse, androsaces for the rock garden and dodecatheons for the bog garden.

Family features The flowers are hermaphrodite and regular, with a toothed calyx formed of five fused sepals, and a lobed corolla formed of five fused petals. Each flower has five stamens opposite the petal-lobes and a superior ovary with one cell and a single style. The fruits are capsules. The flowers may be solitary, or borne in branched clusters or umbels. The majority of plants have their leaves in basal rosettes. Others have leafy stems with simple or lobed leaves in a variety of arrangements. Stipules are absent.

The **Primulas**, genus *Primula*, are a large group of 500 species centred in Asia and beloved of gardeners throughout the temperate world. Primroses and polyanthus are favourites for spring gardens, drumstick and candelabra primulas for bog gardens, auriculas for the greenhouse and several Asiatic species are grown as pot plants. About 35 are found in Europe.

Primrose, *Primula vulgaris* (p. 120), is one of the most beloved of spring flowers, nestling into hedgerows and on shady banks in woods and meadows throughout much of Europe and the British Isles. Sadly, it is much less common than in former years as many plants have been destroyed by modern farming techniques or dug up and taken away. This is a perennial plant, with a short rhizome and a clump of wrinkled, lance-shaped leaves tapering to the base, bright green and hairless above, paler and hairy on the underside, growing up to

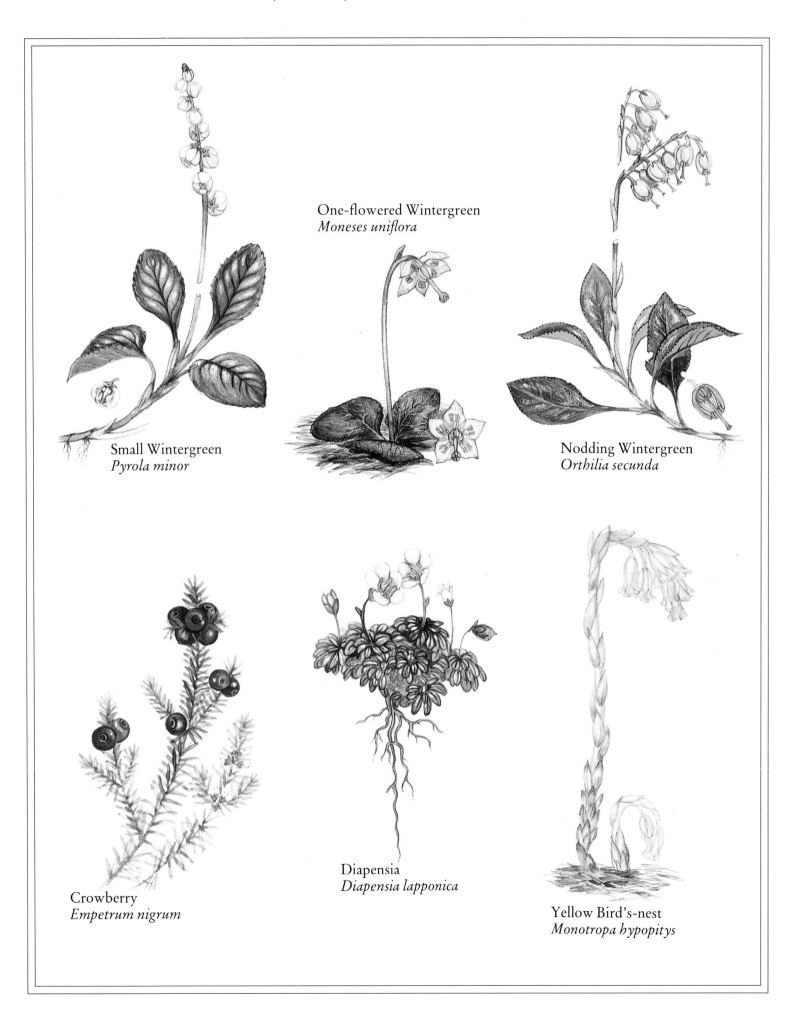

One-flowered Wintergreen
Moneses uniflora

Small Wintergreen
Pyrola minor

Nodding Wintergreen
Orthilia secunda

Crowberry
Empetrum nigrum

Diapensia
Diapensia lapponica

Yellow Bird's-nest
Monotropa hypopitys

25cm (10in) long. In spring the pale yellow, scented flowers appear, growing singly on hairy stalks. At one time this plant was used in herb medicine as a sedative and remedy for gout and rheumatism. Many garden varieties have been developed, including forms with double flowers and hose-in-hose flowers (where one flower grows out of another).

Primroses show a feature common to many members of this family, designed to ensure cross-pollination. The flowers of some plants have a long style and shorter stamens so that the stigma appears at the mouth of the corolla-tube; such plants are called 'pin-eyed'. The flowers of other plants have a short style and long stamens so that it is the anthers that appear at the corolla mouth; such plants are called 'thrum-eyed'. This system prevents self-pollination. Primroses are pollinated by insects: pollen grains from pin-eyed plants are fertile only when they catch on stigmas of thrum-eyed plants; conversely, pollen grains from the anthers of thrum-eyed plants are effective only on stigmas of pin-eyed plants. Clever!

Another much-loved plant is the **Cowslip**, *Primula veris*, blooming a little later than Primroses on grassy banks and roadsides, pastures and meadows, generally on calcareous and base-rich soils. It is found throughout Europe, England and Wales, but is mostly absent from Scotland and found mainly in the centre in Ireland. It has a clump of wrinkled leaves, much like those of the Primrose, but the drooping flowers grow in a one-sided umbel on a much stouter stalk. They are deeper yellow with orange spots in the centre, much more tubular in form with only small lobes around the mouth, sweetly scented. Cowslip wine, made with the flowers, is an excellent sedative. However, these plants are much reduced in numbers and should be left to bloom undisturbed. Hybrids between cowslips and primroses occur where they grow together, intermediate in form between the two species. Hybrids between primroses and oxlips also occur.

In Britain the **Oxlip**, *Primula elatior*, is found only in eastern England, mainly in East Anglia, growing in woods in chalky boulder clay. It is also found in damp woods and meadows in many other parts of Europe, north to southern Sweden. It has a rosette of wrinkled leaves and a stout flowering stalk bearing a one-sided umbel of pale yellow flowers. They are like small, unscented primroses with orange markings.

The **Bird's-eye Primrose**, *Primula farinosa*, is similar in form to the Oxlip but only about half the size of a Primrose. Its leaves are spoon-shaped and unwrinkled, with toothed edges and mealy-white beneath. The flowers are borne in umbels at the tops of erect, mealy stalks; they are pinkish-purple with yellow 'eyes'. This little plant grows in damp, grassy and peaty places on basic soils, mainly in northern England in Britain, across much of Europe but mostly in the mountains.

Scarlet Pimpernel, *Anagallis arvensis*, is a little annual plant found throughout much of the world, growing on cultivated land, in gardens, waste land and on roadsides, on dunes near the coast. It is common throughout Europe and the British Isles, mainly near the coast in Scotland. It has sprawling, often prostrate, stems with opposite, pointed-ovate leaves and many solitary red flowers on long stalks in the leaf axils. These flowers open only in the morning, closing at about 3 o'clock in the afternoon and remaining closed or closing early in dull weather. Because of this the plant has many folk names relating to time and weather, such as Poor Man's Weatherglass, Jack-go-to-bed-at-noon and Shepherd's Clock, together with innumerable variations and combinations of these.

Bog Pimpernel, *Anagallis tenella*, also has prostrate stems, which root at the nodes, and many opposite, rounded leaves. It has pink, funnel-shaped flowers borne singly on long stalks in the leaf axils in summer. This is a perennial plant, growing in damp, grassy places, in marshes and bogs, wet open woods and beside pools. It is found in western Europe and scattered throughout many parts of the British Isles, more commonly in the west and absent from much of Scotland.

Chaffweed, *Anagallis minima*, is a tiny annual, with slender, erect stems only 10cm (4in) tall at most and alternate oval leaves. It has minute, pale pink flowers in the leaf axils, their petals almost hidden by the larger sepals. Chaffweed grows in damp, open places, often in sandy soil, on heaths and commons, and in sand-dunes by the sea. It is scattered throughout much of Europe and the British Isles.

Sowbread, *Cyclamen hederifolium*, forms spreading mats of many plants, each forming a tuft of leaves growing from a corm below the surface of the ground. The leaves are attractive, appearing after the flowers and remaining green through the winter, dying down in spring; they are heart-shaped but with angled edges, with a white margin around a dark green centre, often purplish beneath. The solitary flowers appear in late summer and early autumn. Like all cyclamen flowers they are nodding, with reflexed petal-lobes, and quite distinctive. They are followed by globular capsules, pulled back to ground level by the coiled stalks, remaining on the ground until the following year, when they split open to release the seeds just before the new flowers appear. The seeds are attractive to ants, which carry them away. This plant grows wild in woods in southern Europe but is planted in gardens elsewhere, including the British Isles, sometimes escaping to grow wild. A number of other cyclamen species are also found in Europe.

Water Violet, *Hottonia palustris* (p. 123), is a very different plant, a perennial aquatic species found in ponds, marshes and ditches in many parts of Europe, including England and Wales (mainly in the east). It has floating, much-dissected leaves with linear segments, and erect flowering stems up to 40cm (15in) tall in early summer. These bear whorls of lilac, yellow-throated flowers.

The **Loosestrifes** are a large group of about 200 species in the genus *Lysimachia*, found in many parts of the world but with only nine in Europe. The most familiar of these is probably

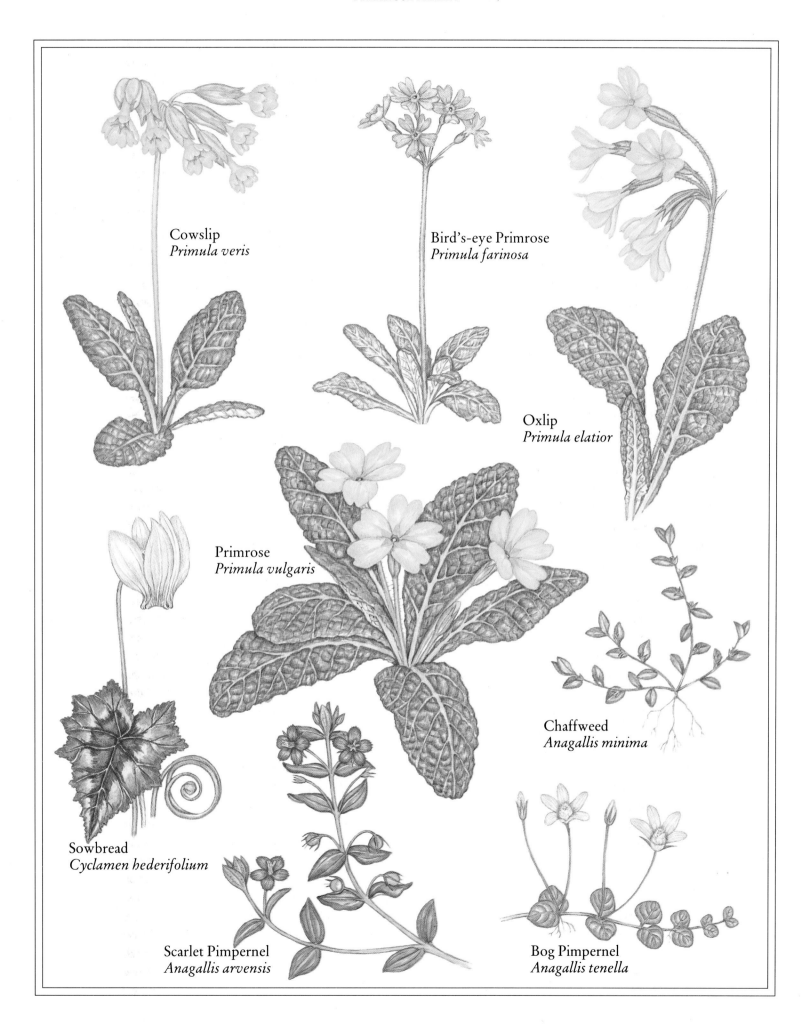

Cowslip
Primula veris

Bird's-eye Primrose
Primula farinosa

Oxlip
Primula elatior

Primrose
Primula vulgaris

Chaffweed
Anagallis minima

Sowbread
Cyclamen hederifolium

Scarlet Pimpernel
Anagallis arvensis

Bog Pimpernel
Anagallis tenella

Great Dodder
Cuscuta europaea

Common Dodder
Cuscuta epithymum

Hedge Bindweed
Calystegia sepium

Field Bindweed
Convolvulus arvensis

Jacob's Ladder
Polemonium caeruleum

Sea Bindweed
Calystegia soldanella

etrating rhizomes and spreading, sprawling stems with fleshy, kidney-shaped leaves on long stalks. In summer the flowers appear, growing singly in the leaf axils; they are large and funnel-shaped, pink or purple in colour.

The **Dodders**, members of the genus *Cuscuta*, are sometimes included in a separate family because they are parasitic plants, quite unlike any others. They lack roots but have yellow or brown twining stems, with leaves reduced to tiny scales, and clusters of small white or yellow flowers in late summer. The plants spread by seed. When dodder seeds germinate, the seedlings must find a host very quickly or die, since they have no roots. The stem of the seedling rotates and if it finds the stem of another plant, twines around it and develops special suckers which penetrate the conduction vessels of the host from which it can then absorb food and water.

There are about 15 Dodder species in Europe. **Common Dodder**, *Cuscuta epithymum* (p. 131), is found across most of Europe, mainly in southern England in the British Isles. It most often grows on gorse and heathers, sometimes covering many plants with its thread-like, reddish stems. It may also parasitize crop plants like clovers and alfalfa and can cause considerable damage. Dense, head-like clusters of scented, pink flowers appear on the stems in summer. **Great Dodder**, *C. europaea* (p. 131), is a similar but larger plant, usually found on nettles but also on hops. It grows throughout much of Europe but is rare and decreasing in southern England, the only part of the British Isles where it is found.

Forget-me-not family
Boraginaceae

Also called the **Borage family**. There are about 100 genera and 2000 species of herbaceous plants in this family found in tropical and temperate regions of the world, especially in the Mediterranean region and eastern Asia. There are many ornamental plants in the family, both annuals and perennials grown in flower borders, including forget-me-nots and pulmonarias. The roots of Dyer's Alkanet, *Alkanna tinctoria*, yield a red dye used to colour medicines and to stain wood; and several species, like Comfrey and Borage, are used in herb medicine.

Family features The flowers are borne in one-sided clusters which are curled tightly at first, uncoiling as the flowers open gradually from the bottom. Each flower is hermaphrodite and regular, with five fused sepals and five petals fused to form a lobed corolla-tube. There are five stamens inserted on the corolla, alternating with the petal-lobes. The ovary is superior with two or four cells, entire or four-lobed, with the style protruding from the middle of the lobes. The fruit consists of four nutlets. The leaves are simple, usually alternate, and stipules are absent. These plants are often coarsely hairy or bristly.

Houndstongue, *Cynoglossum officinale*, was a medicinal plant at one time, its large leaves recommended for wrapping around dog bites; since they resemble dog's tongues it was thought they could cure the bites! It was also used to treat bruises and wounds but is rarely used in modern herb medicine since it can cause dermatitis. It grows in dry, grassy places and in woodland margins on dry soils across much of Europe and in England and Wales (much less commonly in Scotland and Ireland), often on fixed dunes and in sandy places near the sea. This is a biennial plant, with a clump of large, broadly lance-shaped basal leaves and erect leafy stems growing up to 90cm (3ft) tall, all covered with soft grey hairs. Its stems branch near the top to end in curled clusters of dull red, funnel-shaped flowers, the clusters lengthening and straightening as the flowers open. The nutlets are covered with barbed spines which catch on clothes.

Bur Forget-me-not, *Lappula myosotis*, also has spiny nutlets, the spines on the fruits of this species in two rows on the margins. This is a continental plant, growing in vineyards and dry waste places across much of Europe, on sand-dunes on the coast; in Britain it is found only as a casual weed. It is a stiffly hairy, annual or biennial plant, with erect branched stems and lance-shaped leaves. The sky blue flowers resemble those of forget-me-nots and are borne in loose, leafy clusters at the tops of the stems in summer.

Madwort, *Asperugo procumbens*, is a rough-textured, spreading annual plant, its bristly, opposite, elliptical leaves much more obvious than the small flowers in their axils. The flowers may be solitary or paired and are funnel-shaped, violet to purple in colour. As they fade and the fruits develop, the calyx enlarges into two conspicuous kidney-shaped lobes completely surrounding the nutlets. This is a continental plant found only as a casual in the British Isles; it grows in fields, in waste places and on roadsides across much of Europe.

Common Comfrey, *Symphytum officinale*, is one of 12 *Symphytum* species found in Europe. It is a coarse perennial plant, forming clumps of large, bristly stems and leaves, the stems growing up to 120cm (4ft) tall and ending in coiled clusters of tubular, yellowish-white, pinkish or blue flowers in early summer. The bases of the leaves run down the stems, making them appear winged. This Comfrey grows in damp places, on the banks of rivers and canals, in ditches and wet meadows across much of Europe and Great Britain, becoming much less common in the north; it has been introduced into Ireland. It has a long history of use in herb medicine, especially for healing wounds, sprains and broken bones, and was called Knitbone or Boneset in many old herbals.

Tuberous Comfrey, *Symphytum tuberosum*, is a similar but smaller plant, just as bristly but only 50cm (20in) tall at most, with thick, creeping rhizomes, unbranched stems and large, elliptical leaves halfway up the stems (the smaller lower leaves soon wither). The flowers are yellowish-white. It grows in

132

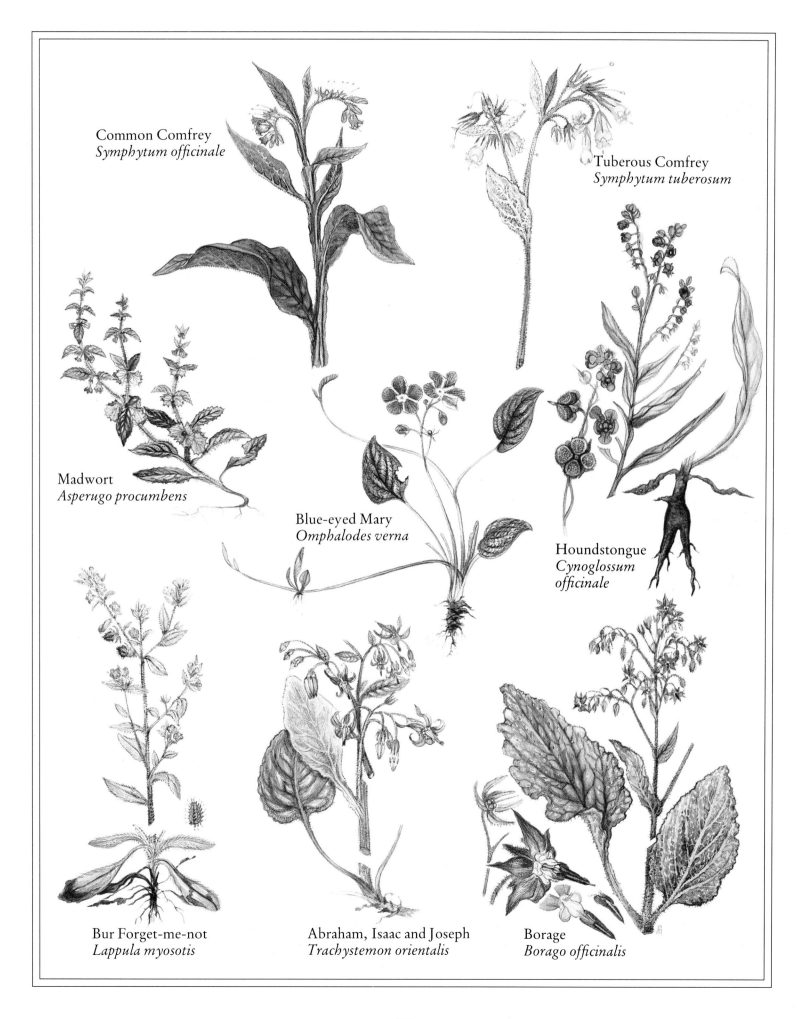

Common Comfrey
Symphytum officinale

Tuberous Comfrey
Symphytum tuberosum

Madwort
Asperugo procumbens

Blue-eyed Mary
Omphalodes verna

Houndstongue
Cynoglossum officinale

Bur Forget-me-not
Lappula myosotis

Abraham, Isaac and Joseph
Trachystemon orientalis

Borage
Borago officinalis

damp woods and hedges, in wet meadows and beside streams across most of Europe, except the north and Portugal; it is scattered in England and Wales, more common in Scotland.

Borage, *Borago officinalis* (p. 133), is an old medicinal and culinary herb known for its fresh scent and taste of cucumber, its young leaves and flowers an attractive addition to fruit punch or salads. In medicine it has anti-inflammatory properties that make it a good remedy for colds and rheumatism. This is a bristly annual plant from the Mediterranean region, now cultivated in many other parts of Europe, including the British Isles. It may escape to grow in waste places near gardens. It forms a rosette of ovate bristly leaves with wavy margins, then a stout branched stem up to 75cm (30in) tall, with ovate leaves, the upper ones clasping the stems. The flowers are unmistakable—bright blue and star-shaped, with spreading petal-lobes and a projecting cone of purple anthers.

Abraham, Isaac and Joseph, *Trachystemon orientalis* (p. 133), is sometimes known as Eastern Borage, and its flowers are similar to those of Borage, with the same kind of reflexed petals and a cone of anthers. However, it is a much larger plant, a perennial with spreading clumps of large, bristly, heart-shaped basal leaves growing from creeping rhizomes, and erect, leafy flowering stems about 60cm (2ft) tall in spring. These produce clusters of the small, bluish-violet, starry flowers. This plant grows in damp woods and shady places, wild in the Mediterranean, in gardens elsewhere in Europe and in Britain, escaping in some places.

Blue-eyed Mary, *Omphalodes verna* (p. 133), is a softer plant than many species in this family, with only slightly hairy leaves. It is a perennial, with long, prostrate stems and low carpets of ovate or heart-shaped leaves on long stalks. In spring sky blue flowers like large forget-me-nots peep out from between the leaves, growing in loose racemes on erect, leafy stalks. This little plant grows wild in woods of western and southern Europe, but has been widely introduced into gardens elsewhere, including parts of Britain.

Lungwort, *Pulmonaria officinalis*, is another plant grown in gardens for its clumps of white-spotted, heart-shaped or ovate leaves and spring flowers borne in clusters on short, erect stalks. The flowers open pink from pink buds and then turn blue. Lungwort grows wild across much of Europe in woods and hedgerows, and is found in scattered places in Great Britain, probably as a garden escape in many areas. At one time it was used as a medicinal plant; since the spotted leaves were mucilaginous and resembled lungs, they were used to treat coughs and bronchitis. Other *Pulmonaria* species are found in Europe, including Narrow-leaved Lungwort, *P. longifolia*, a species with long, lance-shaped, spotted or unspotted leaves; it grows wild in a few places in southern England.

Green Alkanet, *Pentaglottis sempervirens*, is a bristly perennial plant, with a basal clump of pointed-oval leaves on long stalks and several erect, leafy flowering stems ending in curled clusters of bright blue flowers in early summer. Each flower is tubular, with spreading petal-lobes and white scales in the centre closing the throat. This plant grows in woods and damp, shady places in western Europe; it was introduced into Britain many centuries ago, although why is not clear for it is not mentioned in the old herbals. It now grows wild in hedgerows and woodland margins all over Great Britain.

Alkanet, *Anchusa officinalis*, is a bristly perennial plant, with erect stems up to 90cm (3ft) tall, leafy with long, lance-shaped leaves and ending in coiled clusters of funnel-shaped flowers. These open red and turn blue as they age. It grows in meadows and arable land, in waste places and on roadsides throughout continental Europe, only as a casual in southern England in the British Isles. At one time it was used in herb medicine to treat ulcers, cuts and bruises.

Bugloss, *Anchusa arvensis*, is a more straggly annual or biennial plant, very bristly, with stems only 15–20cm (6–8in) tall and lance-shaped, wavy-margined leaves, the upper ones clasping the stems. The flowers are borne in a branched inflorescence at the top of the stem, the clusters elongating as more of the bright blue flowers open. Each one has five white, hairy scales at the centre. This little plant grows in arable land and heaths, especially on sandy or chalky soils, and near the sea; it is found throughout Europe and much of Great Britain, also on the east and north coast of Ireland.

The **Forget-me-nots**, *Myosotis* species, are probably the most familiar plants in this family; there are about 20 species in Europe. Cultivated varieties of the **Wood Forget-me-not**, *M. sylvatica*, are those grown in gardens, forming a blue froth among tulips and wallflowers. The wild plant is common throughout Europe, growing in woods and damp meadows, mainly found in England and southern Scotland in the British Isles, rare in the west. It is a biennial or perennial, with a rosette of hairy, ovate or spoon-shaped leaves, and erect stems in spring growing up to 45cm (18in) tall and branching a little to bear the flowers. As is common to all the forget-me-nots, the flower clusters are coiled at first, unfurling as the bright blue flowers gradually open.

The **Water Forget-me-not**, *Myosotis scorpioides*, grows in wet places and in water, beside streams and ponds, in marshes and wet meadows throughout Europe and the British Isles. This is a perennial plant, with leafy stems which creep a little and root into fresh soil, turning upwards to unfurl coiled clusters of sky blue, yellow-eyed flowers. It is a sprawling plant, only 60cm (2ft) tall at most and often smaller.

The **Field Forget-me-not**, *Myosotis arvensis*, has smaller flowers than either of the former species, the corolla only 3mm ($^1/_8$in) across. It is like a smaller Wood Forget-me-not, with a rosette of elliptical leaves and erect, leafy stems growing up to 30cm (1ft) tall and bearing coiled clusters of grey-blue flowers at the top. It grows in cultivated ground and on roadsides, also on dunes, throughout Europe and the British Isles.

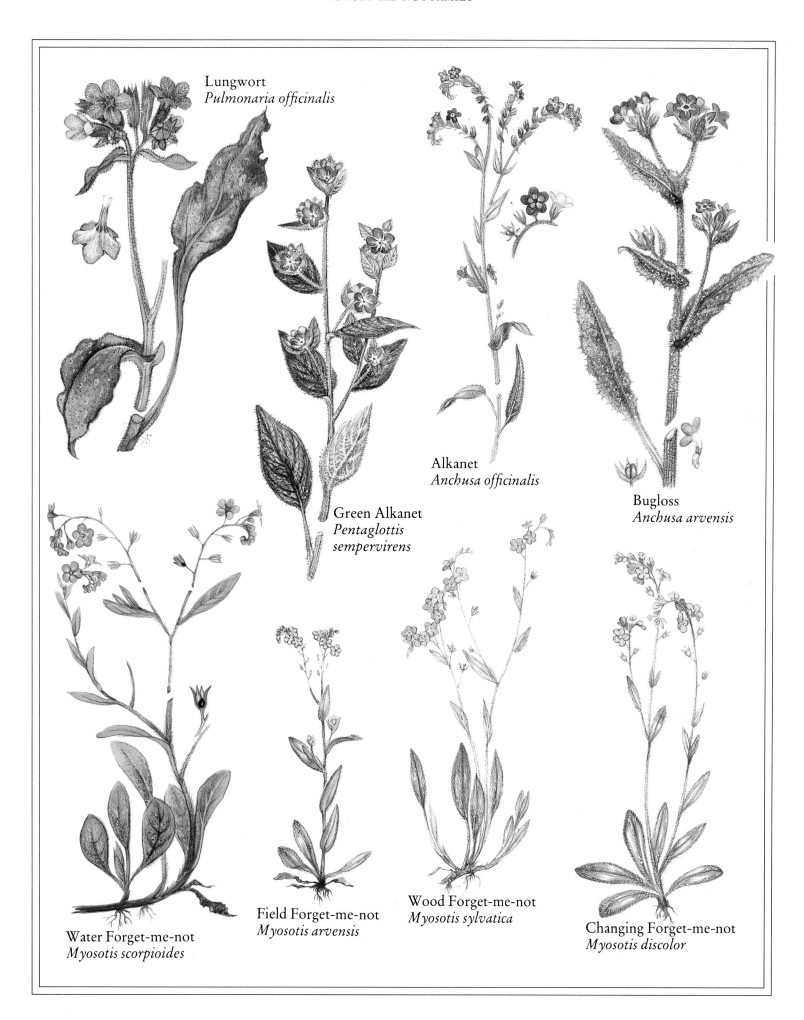

Lungwort
Pulmonaria officinalis

Green Alkanet
*Pentaglottis
sempervirens*

Alkanet
Anchusa officinalis

Bugloss
Anchusa arvensis

Water Forget-me-not
Myosotis scorpioides

Field Forget-me-not
Myosotis arvensis

Wood Forget-me-not
Myosotis sylvatica

Changing Forget-me-not
Myosotis discolor

135

Changing Forget-me-not, *Myosotis discolor* (p. 135), gets its name from its flowers—they open creamy-white, then change colour to pink and blue. This is a small annual plant, with a rosette of hairy, lance-shaped leaves and slender, leafy stems up to 30cm (1ft) tall ending in coiled clusters of the very small, changing flowers. It grows in grassy places on light soils throughout Europe and the British Isles.

Golden Drop is a name given to about 20 *Onosma* species found in Europe, but not in the British Isles. They are biennial and perennial plants, with narrow leaves and tubular yellow flowers. Several are alpine plants. *Onosma echioides* is a perennial, a stiff, bristly plant, with several erect stems up to 40cm (15in) tall, yellow-green leaves covered with bristly yellow hairs, lower ones linear, upper ones lance-shaped. The flowers are borne in leafy cymes at the tops of the stems. This plant grows in dry, stony places and among rocks across much of Europe from France and Germany southwards. A red dye extracted from its roots is used as a food colouring.

Gromwell is a name given to several *Lithospermum* species, of which there are about 17 in Europe, out of a world total of 60-odd. **Common Gromwell**, *L. officinale*, is a perennial plant, rather bristly and up to 80cm (30in) tall, with much-branched, leafy stems; many coiled clusters of yellowish-white flowers grow in the leaf axils and at the tops of the branches. The clusters lengthen and straighten as they age. This plant grows in hedgerows and woodland margins throughout Europe, mainly in England in the British Isles.

Corn Gromwell, *Lithospermum arvense*, is a weed of arable land, a rather bristly annual plant, with a little-branched, erect stem usually about 50cm (20in) tall at most. It has many leaves, the lower ones bluntly oblong and the upper ones linear and stalkless. Leafy clusters of small white flowers terminate the stems in early summer. It is found throughout Europe, mainly in England in the British Isles.

Blue Gromwell, *Lithospermum purpurocaeruleum*, grows in woods and hedgerows across much of Europe, except the north, but is rare in Britain, found only in a few places in the southwest and Wales. This is a perennial plant, with creeping non-flowering shoots and erect flowering shoots in early summer. Both are leafy, with rough, narrowly lance-shaped leaves, darker above than beneath. The flowers grow in leafy clusters at the tops of the stems, opening reddish-purple but quickly turning intense, bright blue.

Oyster Plant, *Mertensia maritima*, in contrast to many members of this family, is hairless and rather fleshy, an adaptation to its life on the seashore. It grows on sand and shingle beaches on the Atlantic coast of Europe from Jutland northwards, and on the coasts of northern England, Scotland and northern Ireland, but is rare everywhere and decreasing. It forms a mat of sprawling stems with two rows of opposite, blue-grey, spoon-shaped leaves and clusters of flowers in summer; they are pink at first, soon turning blue and pink.

Viper's Bugloss, *Echium vulgare*, by contrast is almost prickly, with very large bristly hairs. This biennial plant has a rosette of large, lance-shaped leaves in the first year and a leafy flowering stem up to 90cm (3ft) tall in the second. The flowers grow in many coiled clusters in the axils of the upper leaves, pink in bud, opening bright blue and funnel-shaped; each one has four or five long stamens protruding from it. At one time this was a medicinal herb used to treat snakebites (particularly from vipers) and scorpion stings, but this use has now fallen into disrepute. An infusion of the leaves makes a good cordial. The plant grows in dry soils, in waste ground and grassy places, on cliffs near the sea and on sand-dunes throughout Europe and much of England and Wales; it is rare in Scotland, found only on the east coast in Ireland.

There are about 20 other *Echium* species in Europe. **Purple Viper's Bugloss**, *Echium plantagineum*, is similar in appearance to Viper's Bugloss but may be annual in its growth pattern and has much softer leaves, the upper ones heart-shaped. The flowers are reddish-purple at first, turning blue-purple, with only two of the stamens protruding from each flower; the clusters become very elongated as they age. This plant grows in dry, sandy places in the Mediterranean region and France, in a few places on the coast in Cornwall, Jersey and the Scilly Isles in Britain, where it is a rare plant.

Vervain family
Verbenaceae

This is a mainly tropical and subtropical family, with about 75 genera and 3000 species of herbs, shrubs and trees. Some species are ornamental garden plants, like verbenas, which are annuals and perennials for the flower border, and Lemon Verbena, a shrub grown in gardens and used in herb medicine. Teak comes from a member of this family—the Asian tree *Tectona grandis*; the wood is one of the hardest and most durable, and so heavy that it tends to sink in water.

Few members of the family are native to Europe and of the ones that are, most are shrubs. However, **Vervain**, *Verbena officinalis*, is a perennial plant, growing 30–75cm (12–30in) tall, with stiffly branched, four-angled stems resembling a candelabrum and rough, opposite, pinnately cut leaves, becoming less divided higher up the stem. Its pale lilac flowers are borne in long spikes terminating the stems; individually they are small and tubular with five petal-lobes, and they open a few at a time in late summer. Each flower is followed by four reddish-brown nutlets, separating when ripe. Vervain grows on roadsides and in waste places throughout much of Europe, except the north, mainly in England, Wales and southern Ireland in the British Isles. It is well known in herb medicine, as a cold and fever remedy.

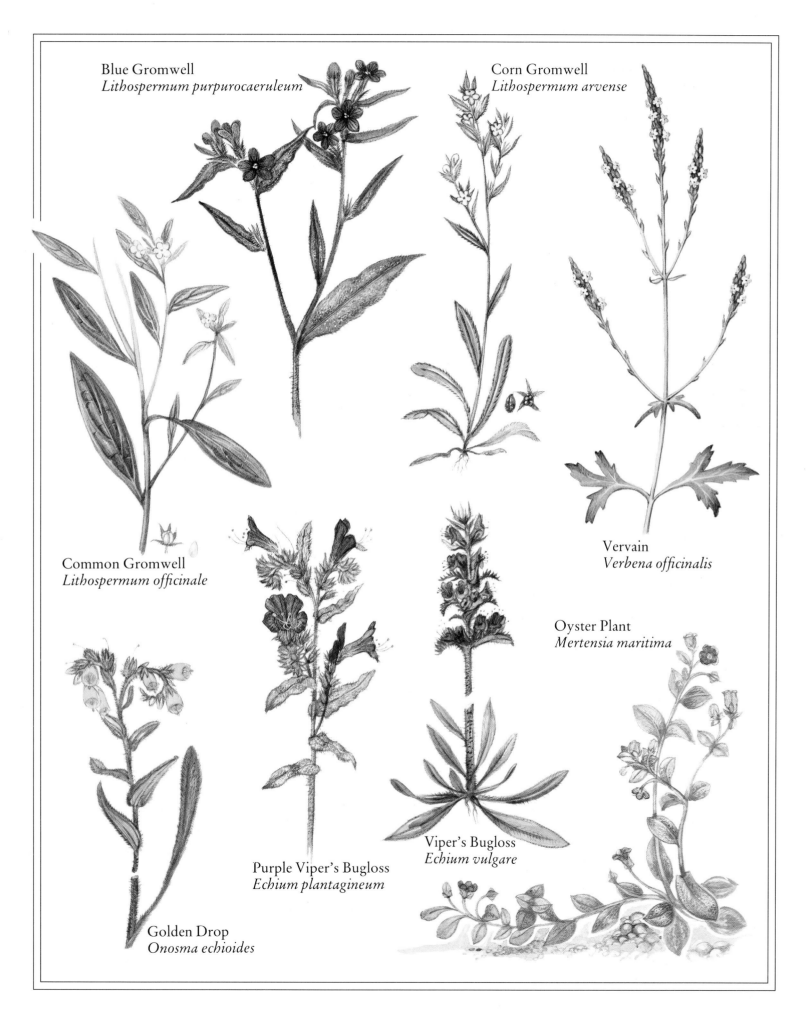

Blue Gromwell
Lithospermum purpurocaeruleum

Corn Gromwell
Lithospermum arvense

Common Gromwell
Lithospermum officinale

Vervain
Verbena officinalis

Oyster Plant
Mertensia maritima

Purple Viper's Bugloss
Echium plantagineum

Viper's Bugloss
Echium vulgare

Golden Drop
Onosma echioides

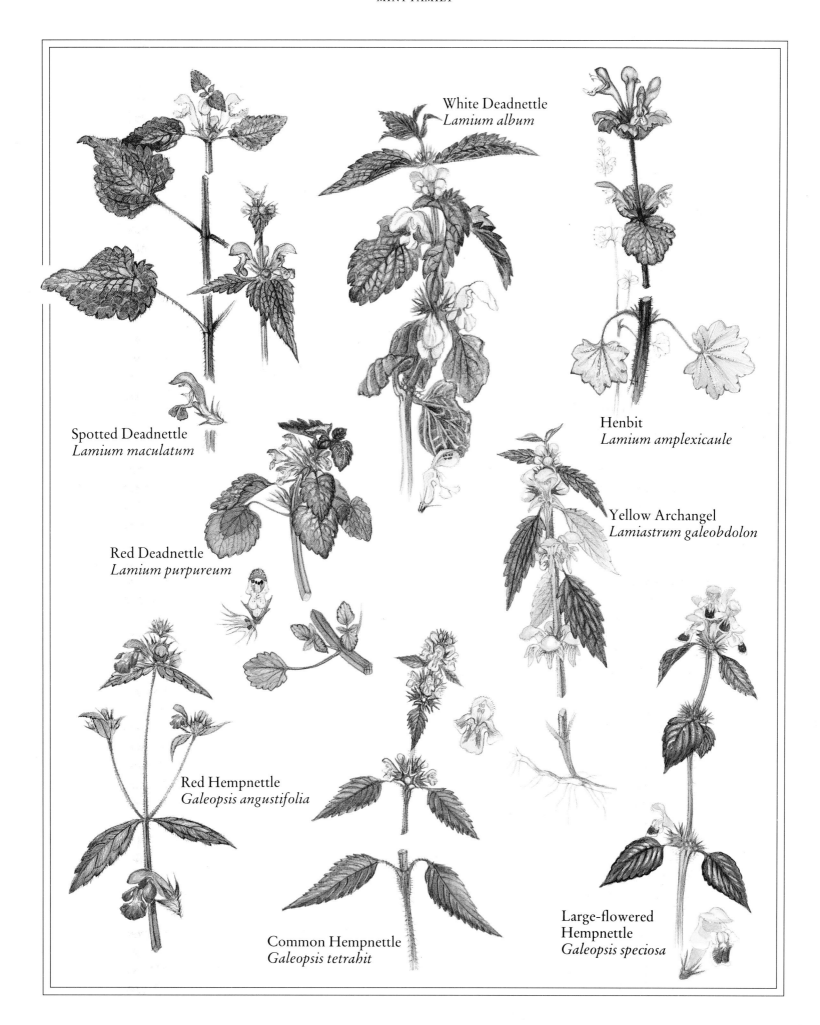

White Deadnettle
Lamium album

Henbit
Lamium amplexicaule

Spotted Deadnettle
Lamium maculatum

Red Deadnettle
Lamium purpureum

Yellow Archangel
Lamiastrum galeobdolon

Red Hempnettle
Galeopsis angustifolia

Common Hempnettle
Galeopsis tetrahit

Large-flowered
Hempnettle
Galeopsis speciosa

Black Horehound, *Ballota nigra*, has a disagreeable scent, dull dark green foliage and unattractive, dull purple flowers in summer. It is found on roadsides and in hedgebanks across most of Europe and much of England, found more locally in Wales, rarely in Scotland and Ireland. It is a hairy perennial, with branched stems, toothed, ovate leaves and whorls of two-lipped flowers at the tops of the stems. They grow in the axils of leaf-like bracts and in toothed calyces.

Catmint, *Nepeta cataria*, grows wild in hedgebanks and on roadsides throughout Europe, scattered in England, Wales and Ireland, only in the south in Scotland. It is grown in flower gardens and gets its name from the attraction it has for cats, who seem to love its scent and will rub themselves against it. However, many insects dislike it and its presence can protect other plants from their attacks. In herb medicine it is used to promote perspiration, so is useful for treating a fever. Catmint is a perennial plant, forming a patch of more or less erect stems up to 1m (3ft) tall, with toothed, ovate leaves whitened by soft, dense hairs. In late summer clusters of red-spotted white, two-lipped flowers grow in the axils of the upper leaves and terminating the stems.

Ground Ivy, *Glechoma hederacea*, was also called Alehoof at one time, since before the advent of hops it was used to give the bitter flavour to beer. It is also used in herb medicine as an astringent, a remedy for diarrhoea and colds. This is a low-growing perennial plant, with creeping, prostrate stems up to 60cm (2ft) long and rooting at the nodes, and rounded, heart-shaped leaves with wavy margins. In spring and early summer its stems turn upwards at the ends to bear blue-purple, two-lipped flowers in twos or fours in the axils of the leaves. Ground Ivy grows in damp places, often in heavy soils, in woods and hedgebanks, in grassland and waste places throughout Europe and the British Isles, rarely in northern Scotland.

White Horehound, *Marrubium vulgare*, is another medicinal plant, used in cough medicines and teas to treat coughs, bronchitis and other throat and chest problems. It is an aromatic perennial plant with much-branched, erect stems, 30–60cm (2–3ft) tall, and wrinkled, ovate leaves, all thickly covered with woolly white hairs; many of the stems are non-flowering. In summer dense whorls of white, two-lipped flowers appear in the axils of the upper leaves; each has a notched upper lip and a three-lobed lower lip. This plant is found in dry, open places, in waste ground, on grassy slopes and downs, and on roadsides throughout much of Europe, scattered in England and Wales, rare in Scotland and Ireland.

The **Skullcaps** are a group of about 300 species in the genus *Scutellaria*, found in many areas of the world, with about 12 in Europe. They are perennial herbaceous plants, with simple leaves and two-lipped, frequently S-shaped flowers, often borne in pairs in the leaf axils. **Skullcap**, *S. galericulata*, forms patches of erect, often branched stems up to 50cm (20in) tall, growing from creeping rhizomes. The stems have toothed, lance-shaped leaves and bright blue flowers in the axils of bracts at the tops of the stems; the flowers may be solitary or borne in pairs. This plant grows in wet meadows and fens, in marshes and beside rivers and ponds throughout Europe and the British Isles. Lesser Skullcap, *S. minor*, is a smaller species with pale pinkish-purple flowers. It grows in wet heathland and woods across western and central Europe, in southern England and Wales and up the west coast to the Scottish islands, also in southwestern and southeastern Ireland.

The **Germanders** are a large group of about 300 species in the genus *Teucrium*, found worldwide, with about 50 in Europe. Some are herbaceous plants, others dwarf shrubs. The flowers are distinctive, with a corolla that lacks an upper lip, but has a five-lobed lower lip, the central lobe the largest and often hanging. **Wood Sage**, *T. scorodonia*, grows in heaths and woods, usually in dry, non-calcareous soils, sometimes on dunes or shingle; it is found in western and central Europe and throughout much of Great Britain, around Ireland but not in the centre. It is immediately recognizable with its long spikes of yellow-green flowers growing above a clump of branched stems with wrinkled leaves. It is a perennial, with creeping rhizomes and stems up to 60cm (2ft) tall in late summer when it is in flower. The sage green leaves are rounded heart-shaped with a texture similar to Sage leaves; the flowers have hanging lips and because they have no upper lip the arching, brown stamens are exposed. At one time this plant was used in brewing in place of hops, but it gives a strong colour and bitter taste to the beer. Tea made from the dried leaves is used in folk medicine to treat rheumatism and cleanse sores.

Wall Germander, *Teucrium chamaedrys*, is a shrubby perennial plant, with sprawling stems only 30cm (1ft) tall, woody at the base and forming a dense, spreading patch with many opposite, dark green leaves like tiny oak leaves. In late summer whorls of small, pinkish-purple flowers appear in the axils of the upper leaves, each one with a toothed calyx, a lobed lower lip and protruding stamens. This plant grows in dry, open places and woods across most of Europe, except the north, but is not native to the British Isles. It is often grown in gardens and has escaped to grow wild on the Sussex downs.

Bugle, *Ajuga reptans* (p. 149), is a creeping perennial plant, with leafy, prostrate stems rooting at the nodes and forming rosettes of smooth, ovate leaves often tinged with bronze. In summer the flowering stems grow up to 30cm (1ft) tall, each with a terminal, leafy inflorescence formed of many whorls of blue flowers. Each flower has a short upper lip and a three-lobed lower lip; the stamens are exposed. This plant grows in damp woods and meadows throughout Europe and the British Isles. It is also grown in gardens. At one time Bugle was used as a medicinal plant for its astringent properties.

Pyramidal Bugle, *Ajuga pyramidalis* (p. 000), forms rosettes of hairy, ovate leaves and erect flowering stems in summer, bearing tapering, pyramidal, very leafy inflores-

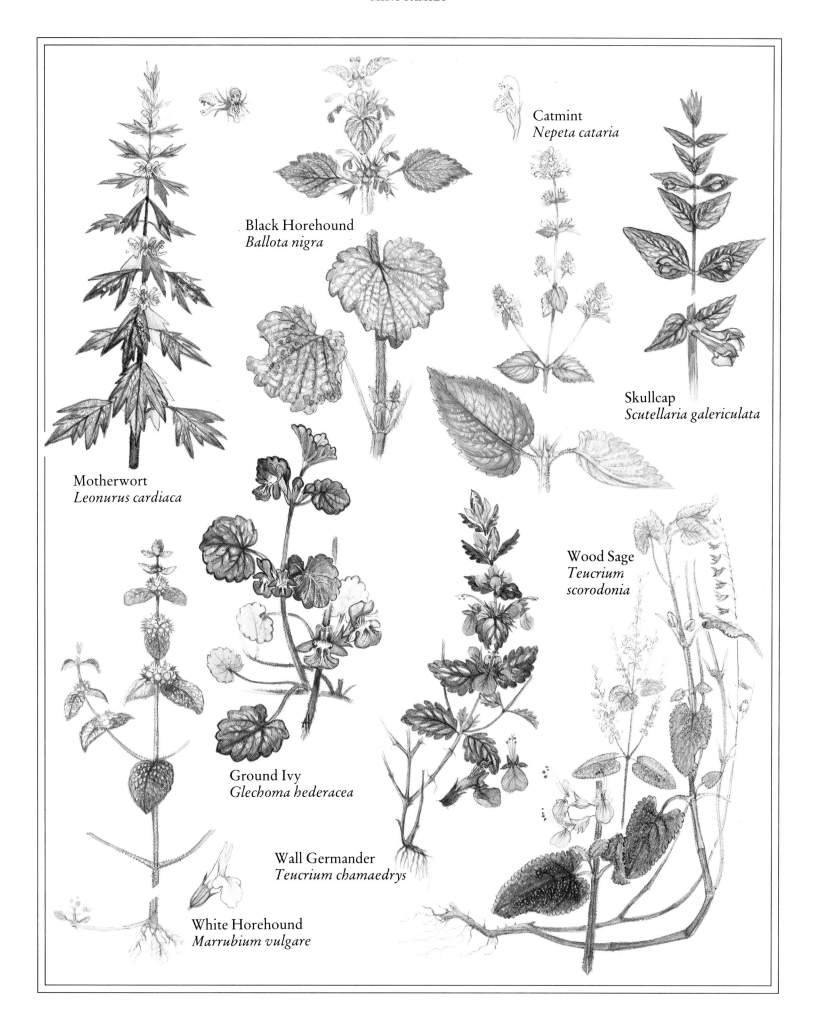

Black Horehound
Ballota nigra

Catmint
Nepeta cataria

Skullcap
Scutellaria galericulata

Motherwort
Leonurus cardiaca

Wood Sage
Teucrium scorodonia

Ground Ivy
Glechoma hederacea

Wall Germander
Teucrium chamaedrys

White Horehound
Marrubium vulgare

cences made up of many whorls of blue flowers like those of Bugle. It grows in mountain meadows in Europe, in the Scottish mountains and is also grown in gardens elsewhere.

Ground Pine, *Ajuga chamaepitys*, is a strange-looking annual plant, its stem almost hidden by the many leaves, each leaf divided into three linear lobes and smelling of pine when crushed. It has yellow flowers almost hidden among the leaves. It grows in fields and dry, stony places across much of Europe, except the north, very locally in southern England.

Nightshade family
Solanaceae

A large and important family, with about 90 genera and 2000 species, mostly herbs and twining plants, the majority found in the tropics and warm temperate regions, especially in Central and South America. There are several important food plants in this family, including potatoes, tomatoes, chillies, peppers and aubergines. Some members of the family are very poisonous, including Belladonna and Henbane; they contain powerful alkaloids used in medicine. Tobacco also belongs to the family and ornamental plants include petunias and Chinese lanterns.

Family features The flowers are solitary or borne in cymes. They are usually hermaphrodite and regular. The calyx has 3–6 (usually five) lobes and is persistent, and the corolla usually has five lobes. The stamens are inserted on the corolla and alternate with the corolla lobes. The ovary is superior with two cells. The fruit is a berry or capsule. The leaves are alternate and simple. Stipules are absent.

Belladonna, *Atropa belladonna*, is one of the most poisonous plants known and just a few of its berries can be lethal for a child. The poisons are the alkaloids atropine and hyoscyamine, which cause visual disturbance, hallucinations, coma and death from heart failure. Ironically these alkaloids are extracted from the plant and used to treat heart failure and ulcers; atropine is used in surgery to dilate the pupils of the eye. Belladonna is a glandular, perennial plant, with a clump of branched, leafy stems 1.5m (5ft) or more tall. The leaves are large, up to 20cm (8in) long, pointed-ovate and alternately arranged or in uneven pairs. Around midsummer and later the plant produces bell-shaped, violet-brown flowers drooping in the leaf axils and followed by berries, green at first, ripening black and glossy, and cupped in calyx-lobes. The plant grows in calcareous soils, in woods, thickets and hedgerows across most of Europe. It is relatively rare in the British Isles, found mainly in England and Wales.

By far the largest genus in the family is *Solanum*, the **Nightshades** themselves, with about 1500 mainly tropical species; few are found in Europe. The flowers of nightshades have characteristic stamens, with short filaments and large anthers;

these anthers protrude from the flat or reflexed petal-lobes and their tips are pressed, or even joined, together so that they form a cone around the style. The flowers are followed by black or brightly coloured berries. Nightshades contain the alkaloid solanine, less lethal than atropine or hyoscyamine, especially to adults, but the plants are still dangerous to children, particularly the berries.

Black Nightshade, *Solanum nigrum*, grows as a weed of gardens and waste places, cultivated land and vineyards in many parts of Europe, mainly in England and Wales in the British Isles. It is a leafy, annual plant with branched green stems up to 60cm (2ft) tall, and leaves that are ovoid or broadly triangular and irregularly toothed. Its flowers grow in drooping clusters opposite the leaves; each has five white, spreading petal-lobes and yellow anthers. They are followed by clusters of poisonous berries, green at first, ripening to dull black.

Woody Nightshade or Bittersweet, *Solanum dulcamara*, is a climbing plant, woody at the base, with branched stems scrambling over shrubs or fences, commonly reaching 2m (6ft) in height. It grows in waste places, woodland margins and hedgerows, often in shingle or on dunes near the coast, throughout Europe and the British Isles, but rarely in Scotland and Ireland. It has simple or lobed leaves and eye-catching racemes of blue-purple flowers with reflexed petal-lobes and yellow anthers. These are followed by clusters of berries, green at first and ripening red. This is an old medicinal herb used mainly to treat skin diseases, asthma and whooping cough.

Thorn-apple, *Datura stramonium*, is much more poisonous than the nightshades—a few seeds can be lethal to children and adolescents. The poisons are hyoscyamine and atropine, with the effects described in Belladonna. Thorn-apple is a coarse, hairless, annual plant, with an unpleasant scent, a branched, often purplish stem up to 2m (6ft) tall, and large, coarsely toothed leaves. Its solitary flowers have an elongated, winged calyx and a funnel-shaped, white corolla. The fruits are prickly capsules containing rough, black seeds. This plant grows in waste places and cultivated land, also in riverine sandbanks, across much of Europe; it has been introduced into Great Britain to become an uncommon casual of waste ground.

Henbane, *Hyoscyamus niger*, contains the same poisons and has the same effects as Thorn-apple. Hyoscyamine and atropine are both extracted from it for use in medicine. This is a coarse, annual or biennial plant with an unpleasant scent like Thorn-apple, but unlike that species it is stickily hairy. Its erect, branched stems grow about 80cm (30in) tall and are very leafy, with leaves so coarsely toothed they are almost lobed. In late summer it bears one-sided clusters of conspicuous flowers—funnel-shaped and greenish-yellow with purple veins. They are followed by capsules enclosed in calyces. This plant grows in disturbed places, often in sandy soils, around farms or near the sea throughout Europe and scattered through the British Isles, more rarely in the north and Ireland.

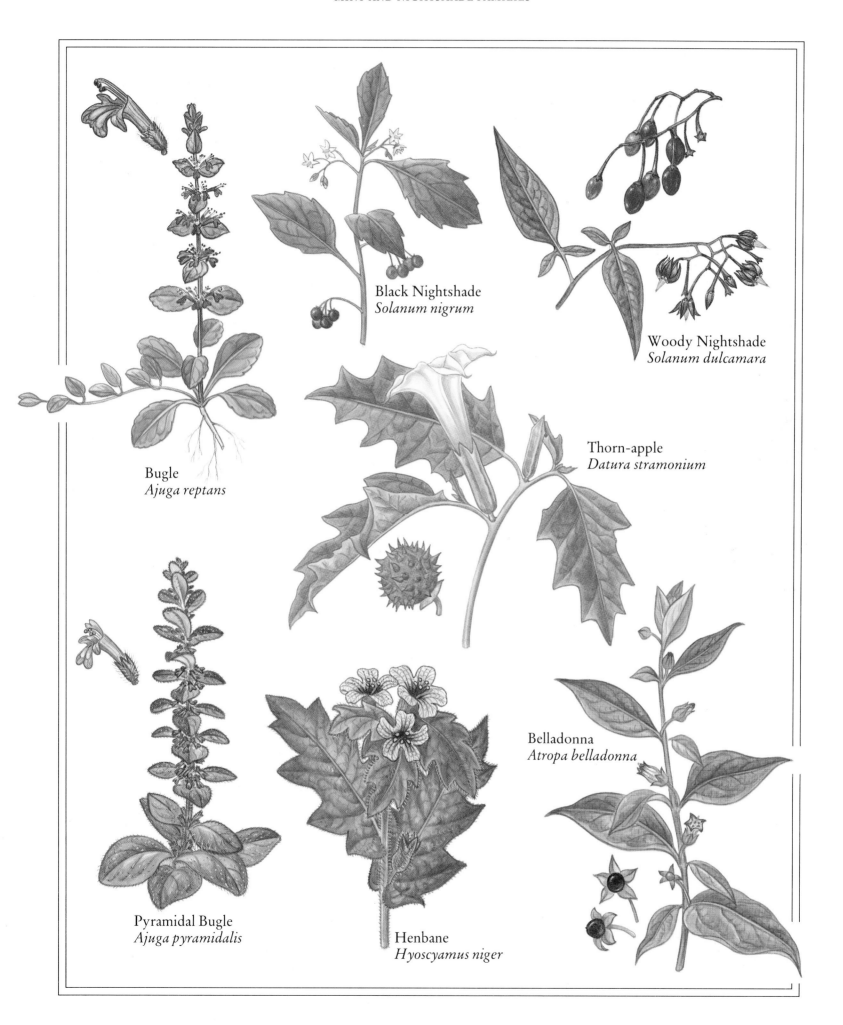

Black Nightshade
Solanum nigrum

Woody Nightshade
Solanum dulcamara

Bugle
Ajuga reptans

Thorn-apple
Datura stramonium

Belladonna
Atropa belladonna

Pyramidal Bugle
Ajuga pyramidalis

Henbane
Hyoscyamus niger

Figwort family
Scrophulariaceae

A large family of herbs and shrubs, with over 200 genera and nearly 3000 species, found almost throughout the world. Many have large, showy or brightly coloured flowers; some, like veronicas, penstemons, verbascums and antirrhinums, are grown in gardens.

Family features The flowers are hermaphrodite and usually bilaterally symmetrical. Each has a five-lobed calyx and a corolla formed of 4–5 fused petals; the corolla may be lobed or two-lipped. The flowers normally have two or four stamens inserted in pairs on the corolla. If a fifth stamen is present, it is usually different and sterile. The ovary is superior and two-celled. The fruits are capsules or, rarely, berries. The leaves are simple or pinnate, and stipules are absent.

The **Mulleins**, *Verbascum* species, are stately plants with tall stems and spikes of many flowers. They are usually biennials, forming a rosette of leaves in the first year and the tall flowering stem in the second. Several are grown in gardens. **Great Mullein** or Aaron's Rod, *V. thapsus*, grows on sunny banks and roadsides, in waste places and rough grassland, usually in dry soils, throughout Europe and the British Isles, becoming rarer in Scotland and Ireland. The stout flowering spike, 2m (6ft) tall, bears many yellow flowers that open over a long period of time. The grey-woolly leaves have had many uses in folklore: they were used as shoe-liners to keep feet warm in winter; they were soaked in saltpetre and used as wicks; women rubbed them on their cheeks to make them red; the leaves were dried and added to tobacco; they were used as poultices and still are used in herb medicine as a remedy for chest diseases. For the plant the leaves have different uses: they are arranged in such a way as to direct water running down the stem into the roots, and the wool cuts down water loss—both useful functions for a plant that grows in dry places.

White Mullein, *Verbascum lychnitis*, is another woolly species, this one with grey, woolly stems and dense, white hairs beneath the leaves; the upper leaf surfaces are green. It is a biennial, with lance-shaped leaves, long-stalked in the basal clump, becoming stalkless higher up the stem, and a flowering stem up to 1.5m (5ft) tall in the second year. This is often branched and usually has white flowers. White Mullein grows in dry, often calcareous soils in waste places, on banks and rocks across most of Europe; in Britain it is a very local plant found mainly in England and Wales.

Dark Mullein, *Verbascum nigrum*, is another biennial plant, this one with a basal clump of hairy, heart-shaped leaves, green on the upper surface, paler below. The whole plant is green, without the mealy, white hairs characteristic of some other mulleins. In summer its flowering spike grows up to 2m (6ft) tall and is usually straight but sometimes branched, with many yellow or white flowers, purple-spotted at the base of each petal-lobe. As in all mulleins, the five stamens are hairy; in this species they have purple hairs on their filaments. Dark Mullein grows on banks and in open places, often on roadsides, usually in dry, calcareous soils; it is found across most of Europe south to northern Spain and northern Italy. In Great Britain it is most common in southern England, becoming rarer in the north and absent from Ireland.

Moth Mullein, *Verbascum blattaria*, is a smaller plant, with stems only 1m (3ft) tall, and shiny, hairless leaves, the basal ones lobed and the higher stem leaves triangular. It has a looser, more graceful raceme of yellow flowers than Dark Mullein, although the flowers have similar purple-haired stamens. This plant grows on banks and roadsides, or in waste places across much of Europe, except the north. It has been introduced as a garden plant into the British Isles, growing occasionally in waste places in England and Wales.

Snapdragon, *Antirrhinum majus*, comes originally from southern Europe but is grown in gardens all over the Continent and the British Isles. It seeds prolifically and often escapes on to old walls and dry places in the wild. In gardens it is grown as an annual but in the wild it survives for several years, often becoming bushy and woody at the base. Each year it forms fresh shoots with almost hairless, lance-shaped leaves and racemes of red-purple, yellow or two-tone flowers. They are typical 'snapdragons'—strongly two-lipped, with a two-lobed upper lip and a three-lobed lower lip, pouched at the base and with a swelling at the throat (the palate), often in a contrasting colour to the rest of the flower. The fruits are characteristic capsules, opening by three pores.

There are about 150 **Toadflax** species in the genus *Linaria*, the majority found in the Mediterranean region, with about 90 in Europe altogether. They have snapdragon-type flowers like those of *Antirrhinum*. **Common Toadflax**, *L. vulgaris*, is found throughout Europe and the British Isles, although less commonly in Ireland and northern Scotland. It grows in grassy places and on roadside verges, in hedgebanks and waste places. It can be a persistent, spreading weed in the wrong place, for it is a perennial plant which forms colonies of erect stems. They grow 30–90cm (1–3ft) tall and have linear leaves and bright yellow and orange flowers. The flowers open in summer, forming long, dense spikes terminating the erect stems; each is two-lipped with a straight spur and an orange palate. The name 'toadflax' comes from the supposed resemblance of an open flower to a toad's mouth, and from the way the plants resemble flax before they flower. This species has a long history of use in herb medicine and was recommended for treating jaundice and dropsy. Steeped in milk it makes good fly poison.

Pale Toadflax, *Linaria repens*, is one of several species with mauve or purple flowers. It has creeping rhizomes and numerous erect stems, growing about 30–90cm (1–3ft) tall, with whorls of linear leaves and long terminal racemes of pale lilac

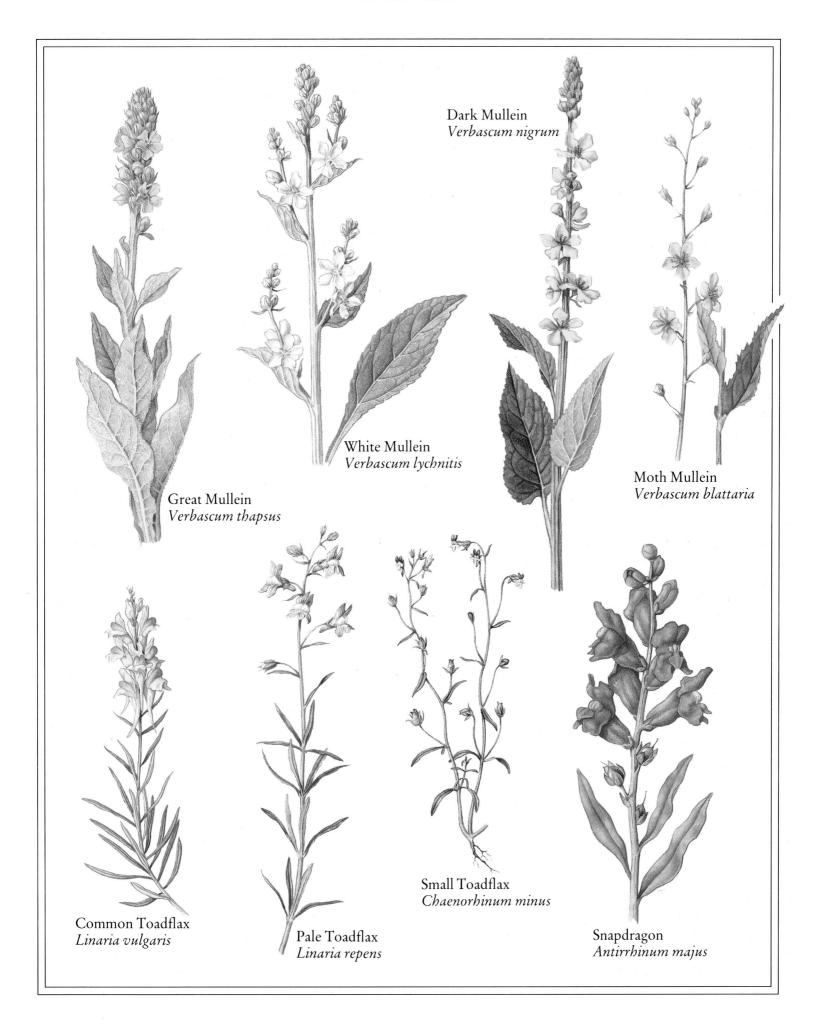

Dark Mullein
Verbascum nigrum

White Mullein
Verbascum lychnitis

Moth Mullein
Verbascum blattaria

Great Mullein
Verbascum thapsus

Small Toadflax
Chaenorhinum minus

Common Toadflax
Linaria vulgaris

Pale Toadflax
Linaria repens

Snapdragon
Antirrhinum majus

Alpine Butterwort
Pinguicula alpina

Pale Butterwort
Pinguicula lusitanica

Moschatel
Adoxa moschatellina

Common Butterwort
Pinguicula vulgaris

Lesser Bladderwort
Utricularia minor

Greater Bladderwort
Utricularia vulgaris

narrowing abruptly into stalks that are almost as long as the blades. The leaves have 5–9 parallel veins and are more or less hairless. In summer the plant bears long, narrow spikes of green flowers with purple anthers, the spikes reaching nearly 60cm (2ft) in height if conditions are right. If a plant is growing in a path where it is well trampled, it may have tiny flower spikes with only a few flowers.

Hoary Plantain, *Plantago media*, also has broad-bladed leaves, with elliptical or ovate blades about twice as long as the stalks. Each leaf has 5–9 parallel veins, is covered in fine hairs and greyish in colour. The leaves grow in basal rosettes. The plants bloom in summer, the flowers growing in dense, cylindrical spikes at the tops of stems about 30cm (1ft) tall, hovering over the leaves; the flowers are scented and the stamens have purple filaments and lilac anthers. This plant grows in grassy places, often on calcareous soils, across much of Europe, mainly in southern England and the Midlands in Great Britain; it has been introduced into Ireland.

Ribwort, *Plantago lanceolata*, has rosettes of lance-shaped leaves held more or less upright and gradually narrowing into very short stalks at the base; the leaves have a strongly ribbed appearance caused by the 3–7 prominent, parallel veins on each. The flowering stalks appear in summer, growing to about twice the height of the leaves, up to 45cm (18in) tall, each one with five furrows running along its length. They end in dense cylindrical spikes of green flowers with whitish stamens. The flower stems and leaves have long, silky hairs. This plant is a common weed of grassy places, roadsides and waste ground, growing in basic or neutral soils throughout Europe and the British Isles. Both Greater Plantain and Ribwort are used as medicinal plants, the mucilage they contain making them effective as cough remedies.

Sea Plantain, *Plantago maritima*, forms several leaf rosettes growing from a woody base, with many thick, rather fleshy, linear leaves, sometimes toothed at the margins, each with 3–5 faint veins. The brownish flowers are borne in long, narrow spikes and have yellow anthers. This perennial plant grows in short grass near the sea, in salt marshes and beside mountain streams inland; it is found in most of Europe, around the British coasts and inland in the Scottish Highlands, the Welsh mountains, the Pennines and western Ireland.

Buck's-horn Plantain, *Plantago coronopus*, may be biennial or perennial. It forms distinctive leaf rosettes, the leaves linear in shape and deeply toothed or pinnately lobed, their bases prostrate then turning upwards so that they may form a circle on the ground. The long flowering stalks are also prostrate at the base, then turn upwards to bear elongated spikes of yellow-brown flowers with pale yellow anthers. This plant grows in dry, sandy and gravelly places and among rocks, often near the sea. It is found around the coasts of southern and central Europe, and all around the British and Irish coasts, inland in some areas of southern England.

Branched Plantain, *Plantago arenaria*, is a very different plant to the previous plantains. It is a much-branched, hairy annual, with more or less erect, leafy stems growing up to 50cm (20in) tall, the leaves long and linear and in opposite pairs, the lower ones with leafy shoots in their axils. The brownish-white flowers grow with hairy bracts in dense, rounded heads borne on long stalks growing from the upper leaf axils. This plant is found in sandy soils, in dry fields and on roadsides across most of Europe, except the north; it is not native to the British Isles but may be found occasionally, growing as a casual in disturbed places or on sand-dunes.

Shore-weed, *Littorella uniflora*, is a hairless aquatic plant growing in shallow, acid waters on the sandy shores of lakes and ponds or beside the sea. It is found across most of Europe, most commonly in Scotland and the Scottish islands in the British Isles. It often forms extensive carpets of leaf rosettes submerged beneath the water surface and spreading over the mud with many creeping stems. These root at the nodes and form rosettes of linear, half-cylindrical leaves, usually about 10cm (4in) tall. The plants flower in the latter half of summer, but only if they are above the surface of the water; male and female flowers are separate, the male flowers borne singly on a stalk less than the height of the leaves, female flowers several together at the base of the stalk.

Honeysuckle family
Caprifoliaceae

A family of shrubs and herbs, with 13 genera and about 490 species, found mainly in north temperate regions and in mountains in the tropics. Several beautiful garden shrubs belong to this family, including weigelas and viburnums.

Family features The flowers are hermaphrodite, bilaterally symmetrical or regular, usually borne in cymes. The calyx is usually small with five teeth, often joined to the ovary; the corolla is tubular, sometimes two-lipped, formed of four or five fused petals. There are four or five stamens inserted on the corolla and alternating with the corolla lobes. The ovary is inferior, with 2–5 cells. The fruit is a fleshy berry, drupe or achene. The leaves are opposite, simple or divided and stipules are small or absent.

The *Sambucus* species are mostly large shrubs or trees, with few species in Europe, the best known being Elder, *S. nigra*, found in hedgerows, waste places and woods throughout Europe and the British Isles. This large shrub is famous for its flowers and berries which can be made into wine and preserves; its bark and leaves are used in herb medicine and its flowers were at one time used in cosmetic preparations.

It has a much less well-known herbaceous relative, **Danewort** or Dwarf Elder, *Sambucus ebulus* (p. 167), which grows

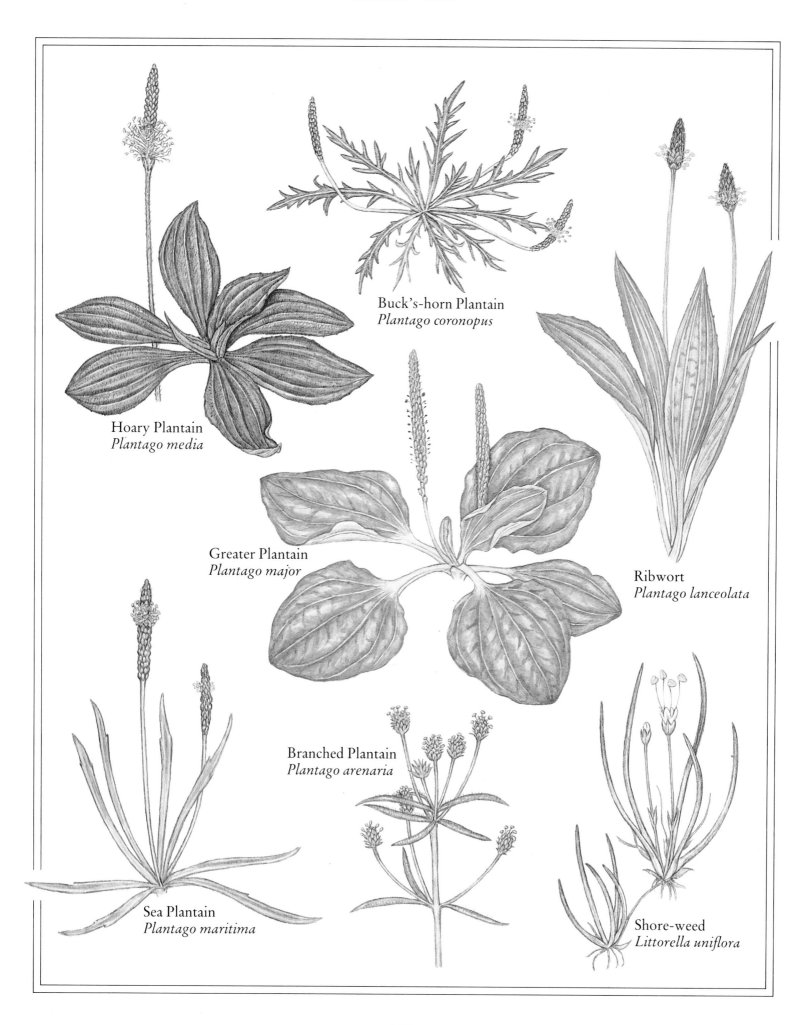

Buck's-horn Plantain
Plantago coronopus

Hoary Plantain
Plantago media

Greater Plantain
Plantago major

Ribwort
Plantago lanceolata

Branched Plantain
Plantago arenaria

Sea Plantain
Plantago maritima

Shore-weed
Littorella uniflora

165

in waste places, hedgerows and roadsides throughout Europe, scattered throughout the British Isles but much more rarely in Scotland. It has creeping rhizomes and numerous erect, grooved stems growing up to 120cm (4ft) tall, with pinnate leaves. The whole plant is hairless and has an unpleasant, foetid smell. The leaves are divided into 7–13 pointed-oblong leaflets with serrated margins. In the latter half of summer the plant bears flat-topped, umbel-like clusters of white flowers followed by many round black berries.

The **Honeysuckles**, *Lonicera* species, form the largest genus in the family, with about 200 species spread across the northern hemisphere in both temperate and tropical climes. The majority are shrubs, many with ornamental flowers, but some are climbers. Their flowers have long tubes and are rich in nectar, attracting insects but only those with the longest proboscis can reach the sweet riches. Many are scented, with a scent that is strongest in the evening, and these attract moths. The flowers are irregular at the mouth of the tube, with four petal-lobes forming the top and a single petal-lobe below.

Honeysuckle or Woodbine, *Lonicera periclymenum*, grows in woods and hedgerows in western and central Europe, and is the only one native and widespread in the British Isles, where it is found throughout. It has twining, woody stems growing through and over other plants, reaching 6m (20ft) tall in a tree but usually much less. It has dark green, pointed-ovate leaves, the lower ones with stalks and the upper stalkless. In summer its distinctive clusters of creamy-yellow and pink, evening-scented flowers grow in the axils of the uppermost pairs of leaves. The flowers are followed by clusters of red berries. Perfoliate Honeysuckle, *L. caprifolium*, is another climber, found in woods and hedgerows in Europe, grown in gardens in the British Isles. Its flowers grow in a leaflike cup formed by the two uppermost leaves fused together.

Twinflower, *Linnaea borealis*, is a complete contrast to these vigorous honeysuckles. It is a delicate, creeping shrublet found in coniferous woods among shady rocks, with trailing stems which run along the ground, sending up leafy shoots only (10cm) 4in tall. Each shoot has small, opposite, broadly ovate leaves and ends in a pair of nodding, bell-shaped, pink or white flowers. Twinflower is a rare plant, found in northern and central Europe and in northern Scotland.

Valerian family
Valerianaceae

This is a small family, with about 13 genera and 400 species of herbs, found throughout the world, except in Australia.

Family features The flowers are usually bilaterally symmetrical and may be hermaphrodite or unisexual; they are mostly small and borne in dense, head-like inflorescences. The calyx is usually small and toothed, often inrolled in the flowers and forming a feathery pappus in the fruits. The corolla is often funnel-shaped, usually with five lobes, often spurred or swollen at one side of the base. There are usually 1–3 stamens inserted at the base of the corolla tube. The ovary is inferior, with 1–3 cells, only one of which is fertile. The fruit is dry and indehiscent. The leaves are opposite or form a rosette. Stipules are absent. Plants often have strongly scented rhizomes.

Valerians, *Valeriana* species, are perennial plants with thick, often scented roots or rhizomes and several erect, leafy stems. Often the whole plant is scented, with a distinctive, peculiar smell very attractive to cats. Their leaves may be entire or pinnately divided and their pink or white flowers are borne in compound inflorescences, often resembling heads or umbels. There are about 25 species in Europe.

The roots of **Common Valerian**, *Valeriana officinalis*, have been used in herb medicine since the times of the ancient Greeks as a highly effective nerve tonic and sedative. This valerian is a stout, almost hairless, perennial plant, with erect stems up to 1.5m (5ft) tall and large, pinnate leaves up to 20cm (8in) long; the leaflets are large and lance-shaped, often irregularly toothed. The pink or white flowers are hermaphrodite, appearing around midsummer. This plant often grows in damp places, in rough grassland, meadows and woods throughout Europe and the British Isles.

Marsh Valerian, *Valeriana dioica*, is a much smaller plant with creeping, rooting stems, clumps of elliptical, long-stalked basal leaves and erect, leafy stems often only 30cm (1ft) tall. Its stem leaves are pinnately lobed. The pink flowers are unisexual, males and females borne on separate plants, males in loose heads and females in dense heads. Plants grow in marshes and wet meadows across most of Europe and Great Britain, north to southern Scotland.

Red Valerian, *Centranthus ruber*, is not native to the British Isles, but is grown in gardens and has become well naturalized in southern and western England, Wales and southern Ireland, growing on cliffs and rocks, often on old walls which its strong, penetrating roots gradually demolish. It comes originally from the Mediterranean region. This perennial plant has erect, leafy stems up to 80cm (30in) tall, with oval to lance-shaped, often toothed leaves, rather waxy and grey-green in appearance. It bears terminal, head-like clusters of showy red flowers around midsummer.

Lamb's Lettuce or Corn Salad, *Valerianella locusta*, is a little annual plant, one of over 20 similar species found in this genus in Europe. It is often cultivated as a salad plant, but also grows wild in dry soils, in arable and waste land, in dunes, on walls and hedgebanks throughout Europe and the British Isles, rarely in Scotland. It has brittle, much-branched stems and many leaves, the lowermost spoon-shaped and the upper ones oblong. In early summer head-like clusters of pale lilac flowers appear in the axils of the uppermost leaves.

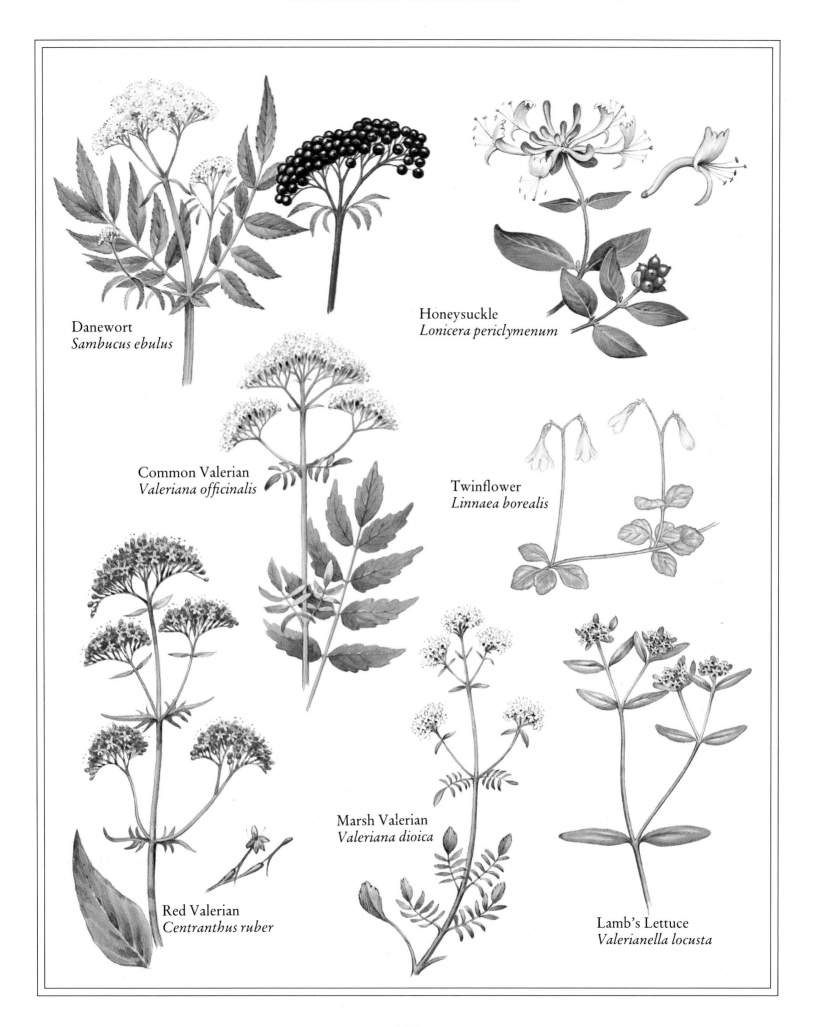

Danewort
Sambucus ebulus

Honeysuckle
Lonicera periclymenum

Common Valerian
Valeriana officinalis

Twinflower
Linnaea borealis

Red Valerian
Centranthus ruber

Marsh Valerian
Valeriana dioica

Lamb's Lettuce
Valerianella locusta

Bellflower family
Campanulaceae

There are about 60 genera and 2000 species in this family, mostly herbs, found throughout much of the world. It contains many garden plants, including Canterbury Bells and the blue lobelias used in summer bedding.

Family features The flowers are often showy, regular or bilaterally symmetrical, and hermaphrodite. The calyx is usually five-lobed and joined to the ovary. The corolla is tubular, bell-shaped or one or two-lipped, and there are as many stamens as corolla lobes, alternating with the lobes. The ovary is inferior, with two or more cells. The fruit is a capsule. The leaves are alternate and simple, and stipules are absent. Plants usually contain milky juice.

There are about 300 species of **Bellflowers**, *Campanula* species, the majority found in the Old World. Many are perennial plants, with erect, leafy stems and blue, bell-like flowers in the axils of the upper leaves. **Giant Bellflower**, *C. latifolia*, is one such species found in woods and hedgebanks, near streams and in mountain meadows across most of Europe, except in Portugal, and in much of Great Britain, becoming rarer in northern Scotland and southern England. It has clumps of pointed-ovate, basal leaves and stout, erect stems often 1m (3ft) or more tall, leafy and with showy, blue, bell-like flowers in the leaf axils, each bell pointing upwards. This species is often grown in gardens.

Bats-in-the-belfry, *Campanula trachelium*, is another garden plant but it also grows wild as a native species in woods and hedges, usually on clay soils, throughout Europe, mainly in eastern Wales and England in Britain, and absent from the southwest. It too has clumps of basal leaves—long-stalked and heart-shaped in this species—and erect flowering stems in summer. The bell-like flowers are blue-purple and point upwards in the axils of heart-shaped leaves; both leaves and stems are bristly-hairy in this species.

Peach-leaved Bellflower, *Campanula persicifolia*, is one of the most common garden species in Britain, grown in varieties with blue or white flowers. It is also found wild in woods and hedgerows across Europe, where it opens its broadly lobed bells in summer. It has basal rosettes of narrow leaves remaining green throughout the year. **Creeping Bellflower**, *C. rapunculoides*, can be a weed in gardens, its creeping stems and clumps of basal leaves taking over large areas. In summer it produces erect, leafy stems, with funnel-shaped, blue-purple bells hanging from each leaf axil. It grows wild across most of Europe, in open woods and fields, and has been introduced as a garden plant to Britain, escaping to invade cultivated land and disturbed, grassy places in many areas.

Clustered Bellflower, *Campanula glomerata*, is rather different in appearance to these other bellflowers since its flowers are clustered at the top of the stems. It is a perennial plant, its basal leaves long-stalked with ovate blades, its flowering stems often only 30cm (1ft) tall and leafy with stalkless leaves, bearing a terminal cluster of stalkless, blue-purple bells pointing upwards, and often with flowers in the axils of the uppermost leaves as well. It grows in grassy places, often on chalk, also on cliffs and in open woods, mainly in southern and eastern England, in Britain and across most of Europe.

Harebell, *Campanula rotundifolia*, is a much smaller perennial, its basal leaves long-stalked with rounded blades, its flowering stems slender, only 40cm (15in) tall at most, with narrow leaves and nodding blue, bell-like flowers. The flowers appear in the latter half of summer. Harebells grow in dry grassland, often on poor, shallow soils, on heaths and dunes throughout Europe and the British Isles. The plant is called the Bluebell in Scotland.

Ivy-leaved Bellflower, *Wahlenbergia hederacea*, is a little trailing plant, a hairless perennial with weak stems growing up to 30cm (1ft) long and long-stalked, palmately lobed leaves. The pale blue, nodding, bell-like flowers appear in late summer. This bellflower grows in acid, peaty soils on moors and heaths in western Europe, mainly in Wales and southwestern England in the British Isles.

Venus' Looking Glass, *Legousia hybrida*, is a bristly, annual plant, with an erect, often branched stem up to 30cm (1ft) tall and wavy, oblong leaves. The flowers resemble those of bellflowers, but are shallower, reddish-purple or lilac in colour, and have an enlarged, elongated ovary below; this later develops into a cylindrical capsule. Plants grow in arable fields and sandy places across western and into central Europe; in Britain the species is found mainly in England but its numbers are decreasing.

At first sight, **Sheep's-bit**, *Jasione montana* (p. 171), looks more like a Scabious than a bellflower, for its blue flowers are all gathered into terminal heads. This is a small biennial plant, with a rosette of narrow, hairy leaves in the first year and spreading flowering stems up to 50cm (20in) tall in the second. These are leafy near the base, with flower heads cupped in two rows of leafy bracts at the tops of long, bare stems in summer. Each flower has a globular calyx, five narrow petal-lobes and protruding purple anthers. Plants grow in grassland, in sandy, usually acid soils, often on banks and cliffs, throughout Europe, mainly in the west in Great Britain, and around Ireland but not in the centre.

The **Rampions**, *Phyteuma* species, also have flowers gathered into heads. There are about 15 species in Europe, most of them from the Mediterranean area, but **Spiked Rampion**, *P. spicatum* (p. 171), is more widespread, found in woods and mountain meadows across most of Europe, only in East Sussex in Britain. It is a robust, hairless, perennial plant, forming a clump of long-stalked, heart-shaped leaves with serrated margins. In summer the flowering stems develop, growing up to

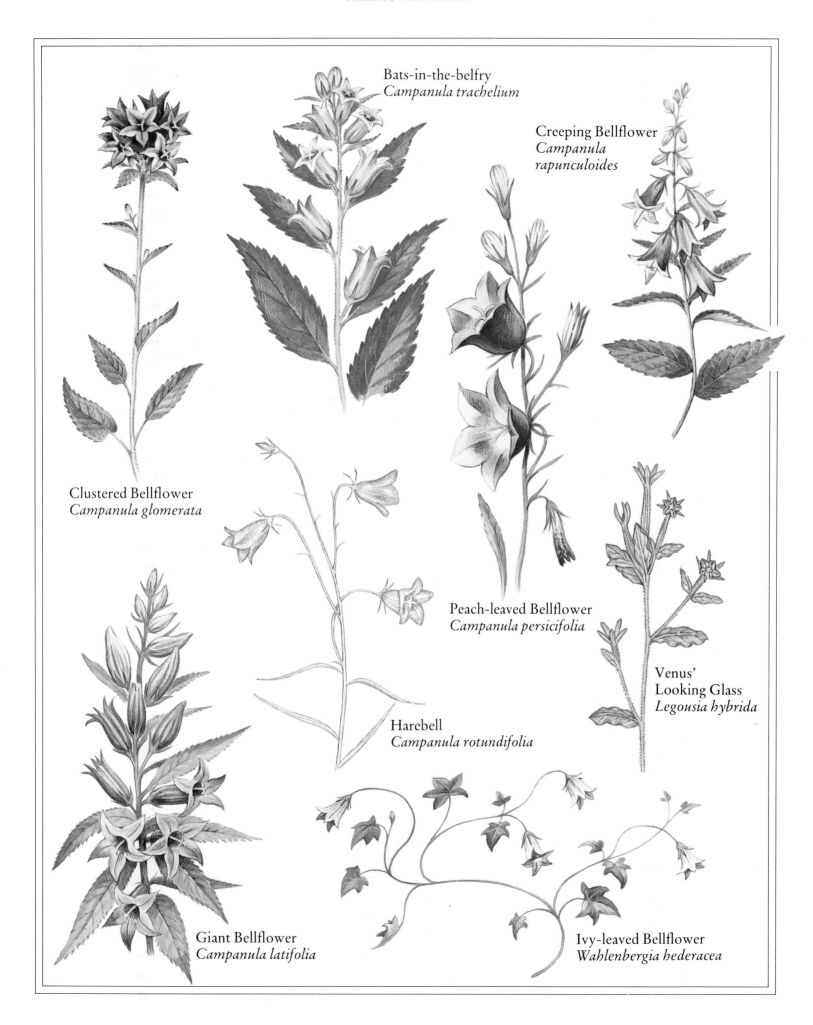

Bats-in-the-belfry
Campanula trachelium

Creeping Bellflower
*Campanula
rapunculoides*

Clustered Bellflower
Campanula glomerata

Peach-leaved Bellflower
Campanula persicifolia

Venus'
Looking Glass
Legousia hybrida

Harebell
Campanula rotundifolia

Giant Bellflower
Campanula latifolia

Ivy-leaved Bellflower
Wahlenbergia hederacea

80cm (30in) tall, their lower leaves similar to the basal ones but becoming smaller and stalkless at the tops of the stems, and the yellowish-white flowers borne in terminal, cylindrical spikes. Each flower has five narrow petal-lobes closed together into a curved tube in bud, spreading as the flowers open.

Round-headed Rampion, *Phyteuma orbiculare*, is a similar but smaller plant, its erect, leafy stems growing only up to 50cm (20in) tall. However, its flowers are deep violet-blue and borne in rounded heads. This plant grows in dry meadows and woods in western and central Europe, on chalk grassland in southern England.

The **Lobelias** are a large group of about 250 species in the genus *Lobelia*, found in most of the warm and temperate regions of the world; few, however, are found in Europe. They are often placed in the Bellflower family, as in this book, but are sometimes put into another family, the Lobeliaceae, since they have bilaterally symmetrical, not bell-like flowers.

Water Lobelia, *Lobelia dortmanna*, is an aquatic plant, growing in acid lakes and tarns in western Europe, northern Scotland, the Lake District, north Wales, northern and western Ireland. It has creeping stems and tufts of linear leaves submerged below the water surface. In summer the flowering stems emerge above the surface, growing about 60cm (2ft) tall and bearing a few of the distinctive lobelia-type flowers, pale lilac in this species.

Heath Lobelia, *Lobelia urens*, is a perennial plant found in rough grassland and heaths on acid soils in western Europe and near the south coast of England. It has erect stems about 60cm (2ft) tall, irregularly serrated, oblong leaves and spikes of blue-purple, lobelia-type flowers in late summer.

Teasel family
Dipsacaceae

A small family of 9 genera and about 155 species, mostly herbs, the majority in the Mediterranean region and western Asia. The Scabiouses are often attractive plants and several are grown in flower gardens.

Family features The flowers are small, often borne in dense heads with an involucre; they may be hermaphrodite or unisexual and are bilaterally symmetrical. The calyx is small, cup-like, deeply divided into sections or into numerous hairs. The corolla has 4–5 lobes and is often two-lipped. There are two or four stamens alternating with the corolla lobes, their filaments free or joined in pairs. The ovary is inferior with one cell. The fruits are dry and indehiscent. The leaves are opposite or in whorls. Stipules are absent.

Wild Teasel, *Dipsacus fullonum*, grows in damp places, often in heavy soil, beside water, on roadsides, in woods and hedgerows, in field margins and by the sea throughout most of Europe, mainly in England in the British Isles, less commonly in Wales and southern Scotland, in a few places in Ireland. Many books make a distinction between Wild Teasel, which they call *D. sylvestris*, and Fuller's Teasel, *D. fullonum*, but they are both subspecies of the same plant. Fuller's Teasel has cylindrical rather than conical heads, with stouter, more recurved prickles—features which were useful when the heads were used by fullers. (A fuller was a man who finished cloth by brushing it with teasel heads to bring up the nap.) Teasel heads are still used to brush some fabrics, particularly the green baize of snooker tables, and can be used for brushing clothes and carding wool. Teasel is a biennial plant, with a tall, prickly flowering stem in the second year, often 1.5–2m (5–6ft) tall, with prickly leaves, the lower ones joined across the stem, making a cup in which water collects and insects drown. The pale purple flowers grow with prickly bracts in heads. They open in the latter half of summer, forming a band which gradually 'travels' from the bottom to the top of the head.

Several members of the family have the common name of Scabious, a name given to them because they were believed to be useful remedies for skin diseases, like scabies. One of these is **Field Scabious**, *Knautia arvensis*, a small perennial plant found in rough, dry, grassy places, roadsides, hedgebanks and woodland margins, especially on chalk or limestone, throughout Europe and the British Isles, but relatively rarely in western and northern Scotland. It has rosettes of lance-shaped, somewhat toothed leaves in spring and erect stems growing up to 1m (3ft) tall, with smaller but more divided leaves and terminal flower heads in late summer. The lilac-blue flowers are borne in flat heads where the outer flowers have very unequal petals, the largest petals forming a ring around the outside of the head. The larger heads contain hermaphrodite flowers, smaller ones female flowers.

Small Scabious, *Scabiosa columbaria*, is another plant found in dry, calcareous grassland, on banks and pastures throughout Europe, England and Wales, north into southern Scotland. It is a perennial species similar to Field Scabious, but only 60cm (2ft) tall, with stem leaves deeply divided into pinnate lobes, the sections becoming progressively narrower higher up the stem. Its lilac-blue flowers are borne in heads, each one with a ring of larger flowers around the circumference; all flowers are hermaphrodite. This is one of about 40 *Scabiosa* species found in Europe.

Devil's-bit Scabious, *Succisa pratensis*, grows in wet meadows, marshes and fens throughout Europe and the British Isles. It is a perennial plant, with a rosette of firm, elliptical, basal leaves and an erect stem up to 1m (3ft) tall in summer. This has a few narrow leaves and terminal heads of mauve or blue-purple flowers, all the flowers in the head the same size, even the marginal flowers. The heads may be small with female flowers only, or larger with hermaphrodite flowers and protruding red-purple anthers.

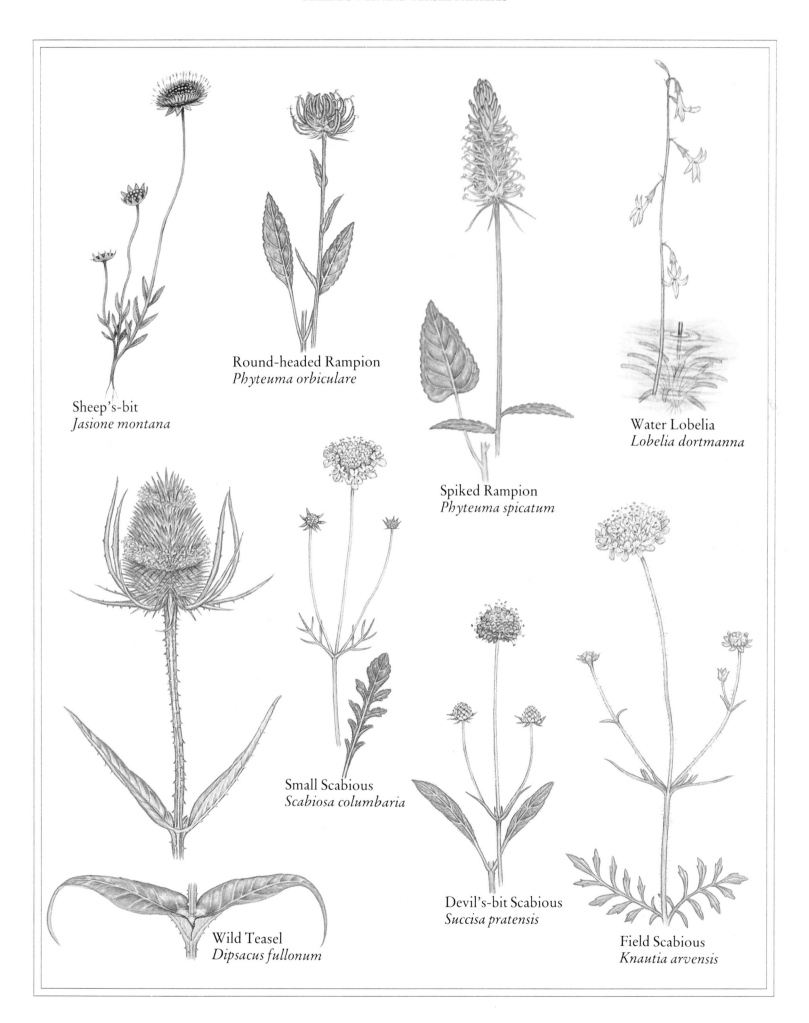

Sheep's-bit
Jasione montana

Round-headed Rampion
Phyteuma orbiculare

Spiked Rampion
Phyteuma spicatum

Water Lobelia
Lobelia dortmanna

Small Scabious
Scabiosa columbaria

Wild Teasel
Dipsacus fullonum

Devil's-bit Scabious
Succisa pratensis

Field Scabious
Knautia arvensis

Limestone grassland around midsummer. In the foreground are some of the flowers associated with this habitat: (from left to right) Rockrose, Bird's-foot Trefoil and Salad Burnet, with Wild Thyme and Stemless Thistles just beyond them. Many members of the Daisy family are also found in such areas.

Marsh Ragwort
Senecio aquaticus

Common Ragwort
Senecio jacobaea

Oxford Ragwort
Senecio squalidus

Hoary Ragwort
Senecio erucifolius

Groundsel
Senecio vulgaris

Sticky Groundsel
Senecio viscosus

Hemp Agrimony
Eupatorium cannabinum

involucre of bracts, numerous yellow ray florets and a central yellow disk. This plant grows in rocky and wooded slopes, in wet, calcareous grassland and marshes throughout Europe, but in the British Isles is confined to the limestone shores of Lough Derg in Ireland.

Ploughman's Spikenard, *Inula conyza*, is a biennial or perennial plant, with a rosette of basal leaves which may be mistaken for those of a Foxglove; they are softly hairy and ovate in shape. From this rosette grow erect, purplish stems up to 120cm (4ft) tall, with downy, pointed-elliptical leaves and a branched, terminal cluster of flower heads in late summer. Each head is cupped in an involucre, the outer bracts green and the inner ones purplish; the florets are yellowish, the inner ones tubular and the outer ones often with small rays. This plant grows in dry, calcareous soils, in open woods and scrub, on rocky slopes and cliffs, and in grassy places throughout much of Europe, except the north, in England and Wales, north to Cumbria.

Golden Samphire, *Inula crithmoides*, is a maritime plant growing on cliffs and rocks, on shingle banks and salt marshes, locally on the coasts of western Europe south to the Mediterranean, around the coasts of England, Wales and southern Ireland. This perennial, rather shrubby species has branched, fleshy stems about 60cm (2ft) tall and many linear or lance-shaped leaves which often have three teeth at their tips. The plants flower in the latter half of summer, with a branched inflorescence terminating the stems; the many flower heads have golden yellow ray florets and orange-yellow disks.

Fleabane, *Pulicaria dysenterica*, gets its name from its old use as a flea deterrent—when it was burned the smoke was said to drive fleas away. It is a perennial plant with creeping stems, forming patches of erect, leafy stems up to 60cm (2ft) tall, hoary from the white hairs which cover stems and leaves. The leaves are oblong to lance-shaped with wavy margins, those higher up with heart-shaped, clasping bases. The stems branch near the top to form a cluster of yellow flower heads; each head has a yellow disk and numerous linear ray florets. The flowers are followed by hairy fruits. Fleabane grows in wet meadows and marshes, in ditches and on the banks of streams throughout much of Europe, except the north, in England and into southern Scotland, in Wales and Ireland.

Small Fleabane, *Pulicaria vulgaris*, is similar but is an annual plant with smaller flower heads, and is much less obviously hairy. Its stems grow to about 45cm (18in) tall and branch near the top to produce yellow flower heads with very short, more or less erect rays. This plant grows in moist, sandy soils where water stands in winter, across much of Europe, except in the north; at one time it was widespread in central and southeastern England, but is now very rare and found only in a few places in the extreme south.

Some members of this tribe have flowers with a curious texture like paper. They are often known as **Everlasting Flowers**, for their naturally dry blooms last long beyond the normal time-span of most flowers. Some, like **Pearly Everlasting**, *Anaphalis margaritacea*, a North American plant, are used in dried flower arrangements, but also grown in gardens in Britain and Europe and widely naturalized. Its flower heads are surrounded by white, papery bracts which look like part of the flower, as if they could be ray florets. It is these which give the flowers their special texture and which last so long.

The most famous Everlasting Flowers are the *Helichrysum* species, of which about 20 are found in Europe. **Sand Everlasting**, *H. arenarium*, is one of the most attractive, with some varieties grown in gardens. In the wild it is a relatively rare plant, found in dry, sandy places, in open grassland and pine woods, on dunes and tracks, scattered across central and western Europe. It is a greyish perennial, all covered with woolly hairs; it has a rosette of spoon-shaped leaves and leafy flowering stems up to 30cm (1ft) tall ending in dense clusters of golden yellow flower heads. Their shiny appearance comes from the bright orange-yellow bracts which surround the yellow disk florets (it is these coloured bracts which give the characteristic texture to *Helichrysum* flowers).

Mountain Everlasting or Cat's-foot, *Antennaria dioica* (p. 189), also has flowers which answer to the description of 'everlasting'. This small perennial plant has short, creeping stems and spreading mats of leaf rosettes, the spoon-shaped leaves green on the upper surface, white woolly beneath. Its erect flower-bearing stems grow only 20cm (8in) tall and bear dense, terminal clusters of small flower heads in summer, males and females on separate plants. The smaller male heads have white bracts like ray florets encircling the tubular florets; female heads have pink bracts held erect. The variety 'Rosea' is grown in rock gardens and troughs. In the wild plants grow in dry mountain meadows and heaths, on slopes and banks, usually on calcareous or base-rich soils, in northern and central Europe, mainly in Scotland and the Scottish islands, in northern England and Ireland in the British Isles.

Edelweiss, *Leontopodium alpinum* (p. 189), is a famous alpine plant often used to symbolize the mountains of Europe, where it grows in dry meadows on calcareous or base-rich soils. It is a tufted perennial, with rosettes of densely woolly, grey-green, spoon-shaped leaves. In the latter half of summer the flowering stems appear, leafy and with terminal clusters of globular flower heads cupped in star-shaped ruffs of large, white-woolly leaves. Each head has a white involucre surrounding yellow disk florets.

The **Cudweeds**, a large group of about 200 species in the genus *Gnaphalium*, are found in temperate regions of the world, but with only seven or so in Europe. They are woolly-haired plants, with alternate entire leaves and clusters of small, often whitish or yellowish flower heads all formed of disk florets. The bracts which surround the flower heads may be completely papery or may have only papery tips. **Heath Cudweed**,

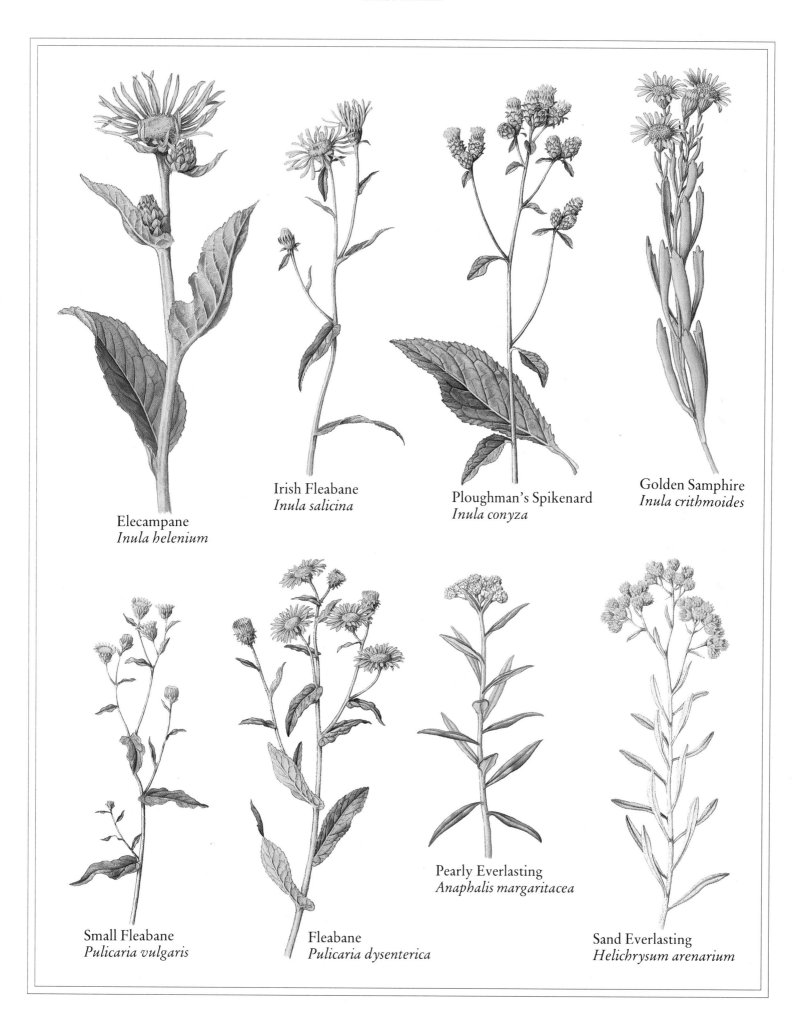

Elecampane
Inula helenium

Irish Fleabane
Inula salicina

Ploughman's Spikenard
Inula conyza

Golden Samphire
Inula crithmoides

Small Fleabane
Pulicaria vulgaris

Fleabane
Pulicaria dysenterica

Pearly Everlasting
Anaphalis margaritacea

Sand Everlasting
Helichrysum arenarium

G. sylvaticum, grows in dry heaths and open woods, in grassland and commons, on acid soils throughout Europe and the British Isles, less commonly in the north. It is a perennial plant, with sprawling, leafy non-flowering shoots and erect flowering shoots growing up to 60cm (2ft) tall. These bear dense clusters of flower heads in the leaf axils, so that the inflorescence looks like an interrupted leafy spike; the heads are pale brown, the outer bracts brown with clear, membranous tips, the inner bracts with a green stripe in the centre and pink or white tips and margins.

Dwarf Cudweed, *Gnaphalium supinum*, is an alpine species, a low, tufted, perennial plant, with many leafy, non-flowering shoots and erect flowering shoots in summer. The pale brown flower heads grow in clusters, forming a dense, terminal spike at the tops of the shoots; each head is cupped in 3–4 rows of green-striped bracts, which have papery brown margins. This little plant grows on cliffs, among rocks and in pastures in the European and Scottish mountains.

Marsh Cudweed, *Gnaphalium uliginosum*, is found in damp places, on the banks of streams and ditches, in woodland rides and tracks, in damp, arable fields and gardens, generally on acid soils, throughout Europe and the British Isles. This is an inconspicuous plant, no more than 20cm (8in) tall, an annual with grey-woolly stems and leaves. The stem is branched, with many overlapping linear leaves and small clusters of curious little brownish-white flower heads appearing in the axils of the leaves and terminating the stems in late summer.

Members of the genus *Filago* are also called Cudweeds, a group of about 25 species, with about 12 in Europe. They are small annual plants, many of them greyish-white in colour from the dense hairs which cover their stems and leaves. **Common Cudweed**, *F. vulgaris*, has erect stems, often branched at the base, about 30cm (1ft) tall, and densely covered with white-woolly, linear, often wavy leaves. Dense clusters of tiny flower heads terminate both stems and the wide-spreading side branches which often grow taller than the main stems. The heads contain only tubular florets, the inner ones hermaphrodite and the outer ones female; they are yellow, cupped in densely woolly outer bracts, membranous, yellowish inner ones, all half sunk into a mass of white woolly hairs. This little plant grows in acid, sandy soils, in dry grassland and heaths, fields and roadsides throughout Europe and Great Britain, north into southern Scotland, occasionally in Ireland.

Small Cudweed, *Filago minima*, has forked stems and linear leaves held close against the stems, all grey with silky hairs. It usually reaches only 15cm (6in) in height and bears small clusters of flower heads in the forks; these are yellowish with pale bracts. Small Cudweed grows in sandy or gravelly soils, in grassland and heaths, in waste land and fields, on walls and in old quarries throughout much of Europe north to southern Scandinavia, mainly in the east in Great Britain and rarely in eastern Ireland.

Members of the **Thistle tribe**, the Cynareae, have alternate, often spiny leaves. There are many rows of bracts forming the involucre beneath each flower head; and the heads contain only tubular florets, either all hermaphrodite or the outer ones female or neuter. The pappus on the fruits is formed of many hairs or scales. Garden flowers include the echinops species and the centaureas, but many more members of this tribe are weeds than are ornamental plants.

On sunny days when its flowers are open, the **Carline Thistle**, *Carlina vulgaris* (p. 191), is a striking plant. The flower heads are surrounded by pointed, shiny-yellow bracts which spread out in dry weather and close up when wet—in the past the dried flowers have been used as primitive hygrometers. This biennial plant has a rosette of cottony, thistle-like leaves in the first year and an erect flowering stem growing up to 60cm (2ft) tall in the second; the rosette leaves wither before flowering. The stem leaves are numerous, wavy with weak spines on the lobed margins and with bases half-clasping the stems. In late summer the flower heads appear in clusters at the tops of the stems; they consist of hermaphrodite, golden yellow disk florets encircled by an outer ring of spiny, greenish bracts and an inner ring of the conspicuous yellow ones. Carline Thistles grow in dry, usually calcareous grassland throughout Europe, in England, Wales and central Ireland, on the east coast of Scotland and in the Inner Hebrides.

Stemless Carline Thistle, *Carlina acaulis* (p. 191), is like a compressed version of a Carline Thistle, with virtually no stem and the flower heads nestled into the rosette of spiny leaves. The rosette may develop for several years before the plant flowers and then it dies; the flower heads have whitish disk florets and shiny, silvery white inner bracts rather than yellow ones, but they are just as weather wise, only spreading out when dry. This plant grows in poor pastures and on rocky slopes in many of the European mountains; it is not found in the British Isles.

Lesser Burdock, *Arctium minus* (p. 191), and **Greater Burdock**, *A. lappa* (p. 191), were thought to be one species until around the turn of the century, when botanists realized that they were at least two separate species. The original composite species was known as *Arctium lappa*, and still sometimes it is unclear, in books on herbal medicine in particular, which species is under discussion. The problem is compounded by the fact that the two grow in the same places and hybrids are often found. Lesser Burdock is the widespread, common species, Greater Burdock the less common one; yet in many herbal books, Burdock is still named as *A. lappa* and also described as common and widespread. It seems that the books are perpetuating the original name, when in fact the plant under discussion may be Lesser Burdock, *A. minus*, or encompass both species. Burdock is used in herbal medicine to purify the blood, and in poultices to relieve inflammation. It is also high in Vitamin C and young leaves and roots are edible.

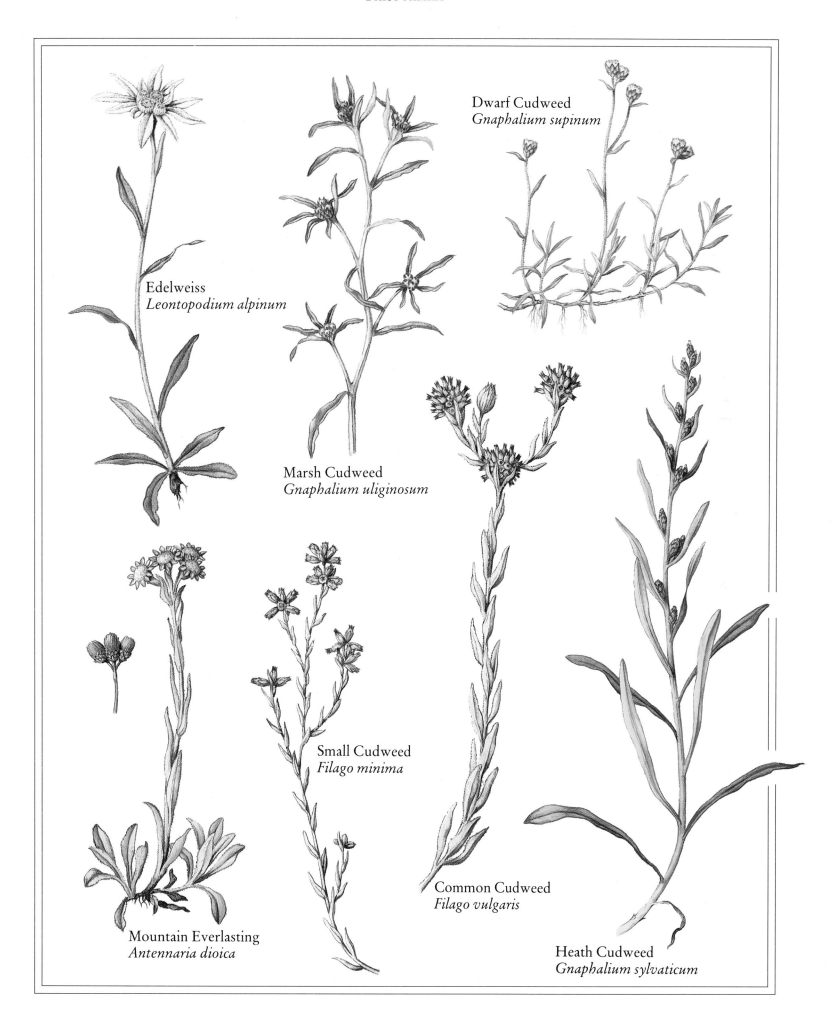

Dwarf Cudweed
Gnaphalium supinum

Edelweiss
Leontopodium alpinum

Marsh Cudweed
Gnaphalium uliginosum

Small Cudweed
Filago minima

Common Cudweed
Filago vulgaris

Mountain Everlasting
Antennaria dioica

Heath Cudweed
Gnaphalium sylvaticum

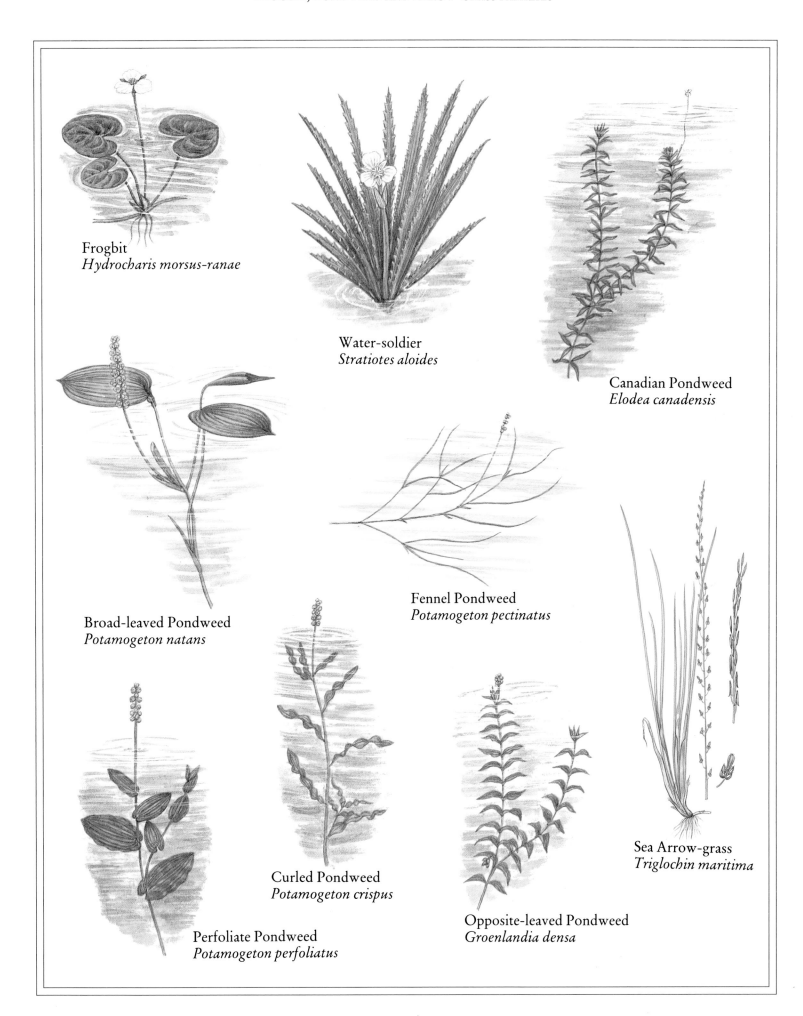

Frogbit
Hydrocharis morsus-ranae

Water-soldier
Stratiotes aloides

Canadian Pondweed
Elodea canadensis

Broad-leaved Pondweed
Potamogeton natans

Fennel Pondweed
Potamogeton pectinatus

Curled Pondweed
Potamogeton crispus

Opposite-leaved Pondweed
Groenlandia densa

Sea Arrow-grass
Triglochin maritima

Perfoliate Pondweed
Potamogeton perfoliatus

Curled Pondweed, *Potamogeton crispus* (p. 205), is another perennial, submerged species with creeping rhizomes. This one has four-angled, branched stems with wavy leaves; these are thin and translucent, often reddish, bluntly lance-shaped with serrated edges. The egg-shaped flowering spikes emerge above water in summer and are followed by beaked, dark olive fruits. This pondweed grows in lowland lakes and ponds, in slow-moving streams and canals throughout Europe north to southern Scandinavia, in much of the British Isles but rarely in western Wales and northern Scotland.

Fennel Pondweed, *Potamogeton pectinatus* (p. 205), has branched, slender, cylindrical stems growing from creeping rhizomes and dark green, translucent leaves, like pointed boot-laces. The membranous sheaths are conspicuous with white-edged margins. The flowers are borne in two-flowered whorls forming long, interrupted spikes, elongating even further in fruit. This plant grows across much of Europe and the British Isles (most commonly in England), in base-rich waters of canals and ditches, ponds and slow-moving rivers.

Opposite-leaved Pondweed, *Groenlandia densa* (p. 205), is similar to many of the *Potamogeton* species, with submerged stems and leaves and flowering spikes emerging above the water. However, its dark green, translucent, ovate or lance-shaped leaves are borne in opposite pairs or occasionally in whorls of three. The flowering spikes are small and dense, usually with only four flowers, and are followed by flattened, ovoid fruits borne on recurved stems. This plant grows in clear streams and ditches, in canals and ponds, usually in waters flowing over calcareous, stony substrates, across much of Europe, mainly in England in the British Isles.

Arrow-grass family
Juncaginaceae

A small family of 3 genera and about 25 species found in the temperate and Arctic regions of the world. They are aquatic and marshland plants.

Arrow-grasses, *Triglochin* species, are grass-like plants, with creeping rhizomes and fibrous roots. **Sea Arrow-grass**, *T. maritima* (p. 205), grows in salt marshes and in short turf near the sea around the coasts of Europe and the British Isles. It forms tufts of fleshy, very slender, linear or half-cylindrical leaves with sheathing bases, growing up to 45cm (18in) tall from stout rhizomes. The green flowers are borne in slender spikes on separate stems, appearing in the latter half of summer; each has three sepals, three stamens and a protruding ovary. They are followed by many green, egg-shaped fruits, each with six sections. Marsh Arrow-grass, *T. palustris*, is an inland species, growing in marshes, wet meadows and on stream banks throughout Europe and the British Isles.

Lily family
Liliaceae

A large and varied family of about 240 genera and 3000 species found throughout the world. Most are herbs, but a few are climbers. There are many beautiful garden plants in the family, including lilies, day lilies, tulips, hyacinths, red hot pokers and hostas. Many of these plants have showy flowers, others have attractive leaves. It would be difficult to imagine cooking without onions and garlic, two species from the large genus *Allium*; it also provides leeks and chives, as well as many attractive garden plants. Some members of the family, like Lily-of-the-valley and Autumn Crocus, contain chemicals which are active medicinally, either of beneficial use in medicine, or poisonous. Several species of *Aloe* are a source of the drug aloes, used as a laxative and in skin creams.

Family features The flowers are usually regular and hermaphrodite. There are usually six petal-like perianth segments in each flower; these may be free or partly fused into a tube and are mostly in two distinct but similar whorls. Each flower has six stamens opposite the perianth segments and a superior ovary; this usually has three cells and many seeds. The fruit is a capsule or fleshy berry. The leaves are either all basal, or alternate or whorled on erect stems. The plants have rhizomes, corms or bulbs.

Scottish Asphodel, *Tofieldia pusilla*, is a small, hairless plant, with a short rhizome and mostly basal tufts of sword-like leaves borne in two opposite rows so that they resemble a fan. In summer the flowering stems grow erect, reaching 20cm (8in) in height at most and each bearing a short terminal spike of greenish-white flowers; the flowers are followed by globular capsules. This plant grows beside streams and springs in mountain meadows and among rocks in northern Europe and Scotland, in high mountains in France and Germany.

Bog Asphodel, *Narthecium ossifragum*, is a more widespread and, to some extent, a more accessible plant. It grows in wet acid heaths and moors, especially on *Sphagnum* bogs, in western Europe north to Denmark and southern Scandinavia, mainly in northern and western areas of the British Isles. This little, hairless plant has fans of curved, sword-like leaves growing from creeping rhizomes; it blooms in the latter half of summer, producing erect flowering stems up to 45cm (18in) tall, with terminal racemes of conspicuous yellow flowers. They have distinctive stamens, their filaments covered with dense yellow hairs and orange anthers. The plant is most obvious as the fruiting capsules ripen, for both capsules and stems become deep orange. This species has the reputation of being poisonous to the sheep that graze on the moors.

White False Helleborine, *Veratrum album*, is a very poisonous plant that can easily be mistaken for Yellow Gentian, a plant much used in herb medicine. It causes symptoms

206

Bog Asphodel
Narthecium ossifragum

Streptopus
Streptopus amplexifolius

Scottish Asphodel
Tofieldia pusilla

Lily-of-the-valley
Convallaria majalis

May Lily
Maianthemum bifolium

White False Helleborine
Veratrum album

Common Solomon's Seal
Polygonatum multiflorum

similar to a heart attack. The helleborine is a stout, erect perennial plant, with clumps of leafy stems up to 1.5m (5ft) in height and alternate, broad, strongly veined leaves. Terminating the stems in the latter half of summer are impressive inflorescences formed of branched clusters of star-shaped flowers, hairy and greenish on the outside, white on the inside. Plants may be found in damp meadows and pastures in hills and mountains throughout much of Europe, but the species is absent from the British Isles.

Lily-of-the-valley, *Convallaria majalis* (p. 207), is most familiar as an old-fashioned garden plant, but is also a native British and European species. It grows in dry woodland and thickets, usually on calcareous soils, throughout much of Europe, mainly in England in the British Isles. It has far-creeping, branched rhizomes from which grow clusters of 2–4 leaves, carpeting the ground when they are growing thickly. The sheathing stalks of the leaves are wrapped around each other and resemble a single stem. From the axils of some of these leaves the flowering stems grow in late spring; each one bears a drooping, one-sided spray of fragrant white bells followed by red berries. Lily-of-the-valley contains convallaramin, a drug that can be used as a less powerful heart tonic than digitalin, the active ingredient in Foxglove.

May Lily, *Maianthemum bifolium* (p. 207), is another woodland carpeting plant growing in acid, humus-rich soils in woods across much of Europe; however, it is not a common species and is very rare in Britain, found only in a few localities in northern England. It has slender, creeping rhizomes from which grow erect stems up to 20cm (8in) tall; each has two scale leaves near the base, withering before flowering time, and two shiny, pointed heart-shaped leaves near the top of the stem. The starry, white, fragrant flowers appear in early summer in terminal racemes; each has four white petals and four protruding stamens and they are followed by red berries.

There are several species of Solomon's Seal in the genus *Polygonatum*. **Common Solomon's Seal**, *P. multiflorum* (p. 207), grows in woods, usually on calcareous soils, locally throughout much of Europe, mainly in southern England, south Wales and Cumbria in Great Britain. It has also escaped from gardens to grow wild in other areas. This is a perennial plant, with a thick, creeping rhizome and arching stems in summer, growing to 80cm (30in) tall, and with many alternate, broadly elliptical, parallel-veined leaves. In the axil of each leaf there hang small clusters of white, green-tipped, narrowly bell-shaped flowers followed by blue-black berries.

Streptopus, *Streptopus amplexifolius* (p. 207), has creeping rhizomes and erect, zigzag stems 30–80cm (12–30in) tall, with broadly ovate, clasping leaves. Solitary greenish-white, bell-like flowers on abruptly twisted stalks hang in the axils of the leaves. This plant grows in woods and among damp rocks in the hills and mountains of western and central Europe, south from France and Germany; it is not found in Britain.

Herb Paris, *Paris quadrifolia*, is a distinctive plant, forming patches of erect stems about 30cm (1ft) tall growing from creeping rhizomes. Each stem has a whorl of four glossy leaves halfway up and a single starry flower at the top, appearing in summer. This flower has four (sometimes five or six) broad green sepals, four thread-like, green petals and six prominent, erect stamens. At the centre of the flower the fruit develops, a fleshy, globular capsule turning black when ripe. Herb Paris grows scattered in damp woods on calcareous soils across most of Europe, mainly in England in Great Britain, but absent from many western areas and Ireland. This is a poisonous plant, at one time much used in herb medicine, but it is narcotic and dangerous.

Wild Asparagus, *Asparagus officinalis*, is similar to the cultivated variety, which is derived from it. In the wild it grows in woods and hedgerows, in waste places, in sand-dunes and on cliffs near the sea (where it is often found as a prostrate form) throughout Europe; it has been introduced into Britain, becoming naturalized in many places, mainly in England. This perennial plant has smooth, erect stems up to 1.5m (5ft) tall, much branched in the upper half. The stems appear to bear numerous clusters of needle-like leaves, giving the plant a feathery appearance and making it useful in flower arrangements; however, these 'leaves' are actually tiny, reduced stems and the true leaves are reduced to papery scales at the base of the 'leaf' clusters. Asparagus plants may be male or female, the flowers borne in the axils of the true scale-like leaves; the flowers are bell-like, the males yellow and the females yellow-green, followed by red berries. Young shoots of wild plants can be eaten like those of cultivated forms.

Butcher's Broom, *Ruscus aculeatus*, is unusual among members of this family for it is a small, dense shrub. It has much-branched, green stems up to 80cm (30in) tall, apparently with thick, dark green, spine-tipped leaves, each one twisted at the base. But as in Asparagus, these 'leaves' are reduced stems and the true leaves are the small papery scales, one at the base of each false leaf. The plants are either male or female, the small, greenish flowers borne on the surface of each false leaf cupped in a membranous bract. Female flowers are followed by red berries. Butcher's Broom grows in woods and dry, rocky places in western Europe, mainly in southern England and southwest Wales in Britain. It is also grown in gardens and has escaped to grow wild in other areas.

The true **Lilies**, *Lilium* species, are a large group of about 90 species, around nine found in Europe. Lilies are plants of temperate regions, many of them prized ornamentals for gardens, often not all that easy to grow and associated most successfully with woodland gardens. They form bulbs, underground overwintering organs that store food. Each year the plant grows from this bulb, forming a stem, leaves and flowers; towards the end of the growing season it forms a new bulb, overwintering again and persisting for many years in the same spot with this

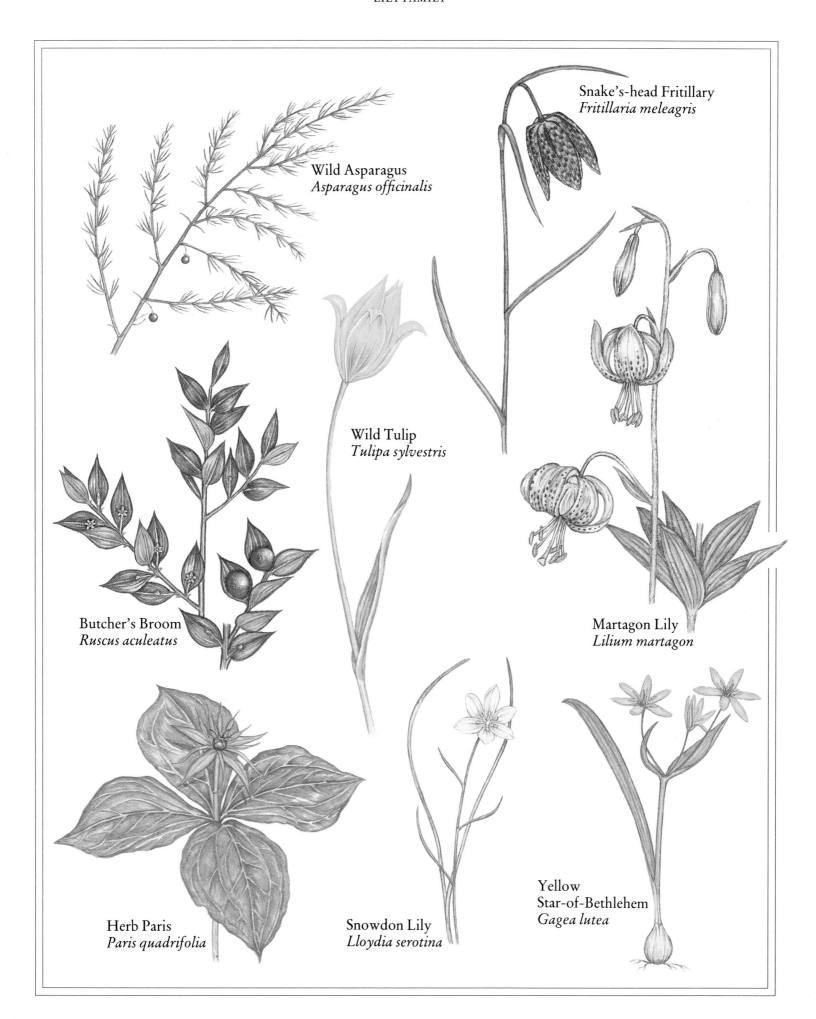

Wild Asparagus
Asparagus officinalis

Snake's-head Fritillary
Fritillaria meleagris

Wild Tulip
Tulipa sylvestris

Butcher's Broom
Ruscus aculeatus

Martagon Lily
Lilium martagon

Herb Paris
Paris quadrifolia

Snowdon Lily
Lloydia serotina

Yellow
Star-of-Bethlehem
Gagea lutea

cycle of growth and renewal. The bulb is actually an extremely shortened stem, with fleshy, food-storing leaves folded around it and a growing tip from which the new plant forms.

The **Martagon Lily**, *Lilium martagon* (p. 209), grows in woods and mountain pastures across much of Europe, except in the north, and has probably been introduced into Great Britain where it is often grown in gardens; in the wild it is found in a number of woodland localities in England. It forms an erect stem up to 1m (3ft) tall, with whorls of ovate or lance-shaped leaves and has a raceme of nodding flowers at the top of the stem in late summer. These are pink or pale purple with darker raised spots on the inside, the petals strongly recurved so that they form incomplete circles. The protruding stamens have versatile, reddish-brown anthers.

Fritillaries belong to the genus *Fritillaria*. They have bulbs formed of a single fleshy scale-leaf. Some are large and striking plants, like the Imperial Fritillaries grown in gardens, but others are small, delicate plants, like the native **Snake's-head Fritillary**, *F. meleagris* (p. 209). This beautiful species grows in damp meadows and pastures across most of Europe, mainly in southern England in Britain and not in Ireland. It has decreased to the point of extinction in many areas with the dis-appearance of the water meadows and is threatened every-where by improved drainage techniques. In spring a single stem grows from each bulb, reaching about 30cm (1ft) tall and bearing several linear leaves and a single nodding flower at the top. The flower is like a lantern, with six petals chequered in light and dark purple. The plant is often planted in gardens but needs damp conditions to do well.

Wild Tulip, *Tulipa sylvestris* (p. 209), has a bulb formed of many fleshy scale leaves protected by dry brown scales (the tunic). Each spring it produces a single erect stem from each bulb, growing 30–60cm (1–2ft) tall, with three rather fleshy, linear leaves, their bases clasping the stems, and a single ter-minal flower. The flowers are like those of cultivated tulips, deeply bell-shaped and held upright, opening from drooping buds. In this species the flowers are yellow and the petal-like perianth segments are pointed; the outer 'petals' are tinged with red or green and turn back on themselves, while the inner ones are held erect at first, spreading as the flowers age. Fruits are oblong capsules but are rarely formed. Wild Tulips grow in fields and cultivated ground, in grassy places and woods across much of Europe, as native plants in the south, introduced further north. In Britain they have become naturalized in meadows and orchards in many parts of England.

Snowdon Lily, *Lloydia serotina* (p. 209), is an alpine species, growing on mountain ledges, among rocks and in pas-tures, in the mountains of central Europe and across Asia; it is rare in Britain, found only in the mountains of Snowdonia. It is a small plant, with a bulb from which grow two or more thread-like basal leaves and an erect flowering stem 15cm (6in) tall at most; this bears several linear leaves and a single flower

around midsummer. The flower is bell-shaped, upright or half-nodding, with six white, red-veined petals persisting beneath the globular capsule as it enlarges.

Yellow Star-of-Bethlehem, *Gagea lutea* (p. 209), is a spring-flowering plant, with a single bulb, one broad, linear to lance-shaped basal leaf and a flowering stem which grows in its axil, reaching 25cm (10in) in height at most. The starry, yellow flowers are borne in a terminal umbel on this stem, the umbel subtended by a pair of opposite leaves. Each petal has a streak of green on its outside. Plants grow in damp woods, hedge-rows and meadows across most of Europe, scattered very locally in England north to central Scotland. There are about 20 *Gagea* species in Europe, all with similar starry, yellow flowers distinguished by differences in their leaves and in their distributions.

Star-of-Bethlehem, *Ornithogalum umbellatum*, at first glance may appear to resemble the previous species, but in fact is rather different in form. It has many white bulbs, new ones formed each year, so the plants spread into large patches. All the leaves are basal, linear and grooved, grass-like, each with a white stripe down the midrib. As well as leaves, larger bulbs produce leafless flowering stems growing up to 30cm (1ft) tall, the starry, white flowers borne in flat-topped terminal racemes. The backs of their petals are green-striped. The plants have bloomed, formed seed capsules and disappeared by late summer. The species is often grown in gardens, but is rather invasive and the bulbs are impossible to eradicate. In the wild it grows in grassy places and cultivated land across much of Europe, except the north; it has probably been introduced into Britain, but is now widespread in the wild in England and southern Scotland, more local in Wales and northern Scotland.

Drooping Star-of-Bethlehem, *Ornithogalum nutans*, comes originally from the Mediterranean region but has become widely naturalized in grassy places elsewhere in Europe, including eastern and central England. It has white-striped, grass-like leaves growing from an egg-shaped bulb, and an erect flowering stem up to 60cm (2ft) tall with a ter-minal, one-sided raceme of flowers in late spring. The flowers are white with a wide green band down the outside of each petal, nodding as they open from erect buds. The stamens are distinctive, with broad filaments deeply cleft at the tip, the anthers in the clefts. There are over 20 *Ornithogalum* species in Europe, all with basal leaves and racemes of white starry flowers marked with green.

Spring Squill, *Scilla verna*, is one of about 80 *Scilla* species, over 20 of which occur in Europe. Several are grown in rock gardens, notably *Scilla siberica*. Spring Squill is a small, del-icate, bulbous plant, with a tuft of grass-like basal leaves appearing in spring before the flowers. Larger bulbs also pro-duce leafless flowering stems, each bearing a dense, flat-topped cluster of starry, blue-violet flowers in late spring; the flowers are held more or less erect. This plant grows in dry, grassy

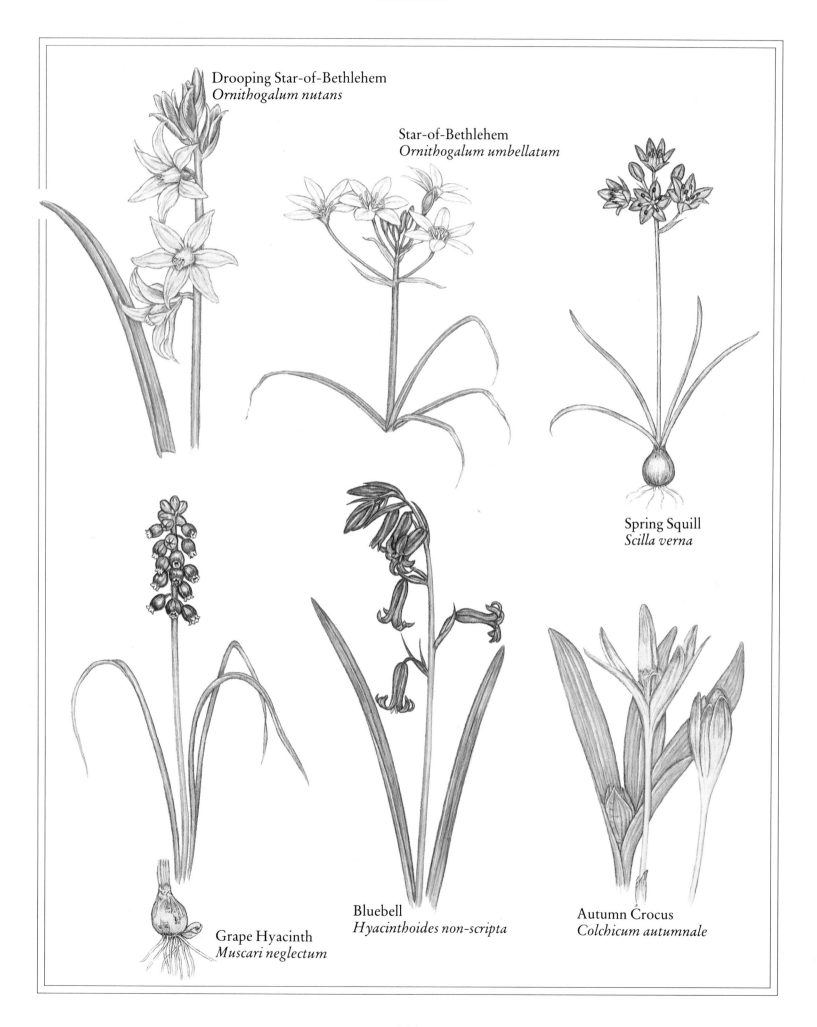

Drooping Star-of-Bethlehem
Ornithogalum nutans

Star-of-Bethlehem
Ornithogalum umbellatum

Spring Squill
Scilla verna

Grape Hyacinth
Muscari neglectum

Bluebell
Hyacinthoides non-scripta

Autumn Crocus
Colchicum autumnale

places and heaths in western Europe, very locally in the British Isles, mainly along the west coast of Great Britain, in the Hebrides, and on the east coast of Ireland. Autumn Squill, *S. autumnalis*, is a similar but somewhat larger plant, with a raceme of purple flowers borne in late summer and autumn; the leaves appear after the plants have flowered. This squill is found in dry grassland in the Mediterranean region, in France and England, mainly on the southwest coast, but also in a few places on the Isle of Wight and in the southeast.

The oak woods of western Europe and the British Isles provide homes for one of the most beautiful spring flowers, the **Bluebell**, *Hyacinthoides non-scripta* (p. 211). When growing in profusion they carpet the woodland floor with blue flowers in April and May. Bluebells have white bulbs and linear, grass-like leaves. Mature bulbs also produce flowers borne in drooping, one-sided racemes on leafless stalks up to 50cm (20in) tall. The flowers are narrowly bell-shaped with recurved tips, violet-blue in colour, nodding when fully open but with erect buds. They are followed by three-lobed capsules. Bluebells grow not only in oak woods, but also in hedges and sometimes in heathland, throughout western Europe and the British Isles but their numbers are declining from overpicking and with the disappearance of the woods and heaths.

Grape Hyacinths, *Muscari neglectum* (p. 211), are found in olive groves and vineyards, in cultivated ground and dry grassland in continental Europe, except for the north. They are not native to the British Isles but have been grown in gardens for many years, escaping into the wild in some places, particularly in East Anglia. Grape Hyacinths are bulbous plants with tufts of linear, almost cylindrical leaves appearing in winter long before the flowers. The flowering stems grow in spring, producing a dense, terminal spike of dark blue, flask-shaped flowers, each one with a small mouth surrounded by white recurved teeth. A few of the uppermost flowers of each spike are often smaller than the lower ones and sterile. Fertile flowers produce seed capsules.

Autumn Crocus, *Colchicum autumnale* (p. 211), is also known as Meadow Saffron and Naked Ladies. This last name comes from the appearance of the flowers, which seem to grow directly from the ground, without leaves or stems, in autumn. The flowers are like crocuses—shaped like goblets, pale purple in colour with orange anthers. In fact the flowers grow from corms buried in the soil. When the flowers die back they leave the developing fruiting capsule at soil level; this enlarges and emerges with the leaves in the following spring. The leaves are large, bright green, glossy and lance-shaped, growing directly from the corm like the flowers. This strange plant grows in damp meadows and woods across most of Europe, except the north, in England and eastern Wales in Great Britain, in a few places in southeastern Ireland. It is very poisonous, containing colchicine which disrupts cell division; this makes it a very useful substance for use in experimental genetics.

The **Onions** are a very large group, with about 700 species in the genus *Allium*, distributed throughout the northern hemisphere and Africa. About 90 are found in Europe. All the *Allium* species are more or less scented and many are eaten as vegetables or used for flavouring, including onions, chives, shallots, leeks and garlic. A variety of ornamental alliums are grown in gardens. Alliums are bulbous plants, with a bulb formed of fleshy scale leaves surrounded and protected by a tunic formed of one or two membranous leaves. Bulbs may be solitary or develop in clusters. From the bulb grows a clump of leaves, varying in shape from linear to ovate, from flattened to three-angled; mature bulbs also produce flowering stems with terminal umbels of flowers, the umbel at first enclosed in a leaf-like structure called a spathe. Some *Allium* species produce bulbils as well as flowers in their flower clusters, sometimes so many of them that they almost replace the flowers.

Cultivated Onions belong to the species *Allium cepa*, a plant native to southeastern Asia and grown throughout Europe and the British Isles. Its bulbs and cylindrical, hollow leaves are familiar to everyone, but its flowers less so. They are greenish-white and borne in dense, many-flowered, round umbels which may measure up to 10cm (4in) across.

Chives, *Allium schoenoprasum*, is another cultivated species, but this one is native to Europe. It grows in clumps, its soft, cylindrical leaves growing from clusters of narrow, elongated bulbs, its leafless flower stems with rounded umbels of pale purple flowers appearing around midsummer. It grows in damp meadows and among rocks, often beside streams, throughout much of Europe, in mountains in the south of its range, in a few scattered localities in England and Wales.

Ramsons, *Allium ursinum*, has a strong, distinctive scent like slightly rancid garlic, and the scent of the plants permeates the woods where they grow. Sometimes they grow in profusion, forming carpets of bright green, elliptical leaves on the woodland floor, especially in damp woods, but they also grow in smaller numbers in hedgerows and other shady places throughout Europe and the British Isles. The leaves grow from narrow, solitary bulbs, appearing in spring and early summer, two leaves and one flowering stem from each bulb. The white, starry flowers are borne in flat-topped umbels cupped in a membranous spathe, growing on two-angled or three-angled stems about 30cm (1ft) tall.

The three-angled leaves and stems of **Triquetrous Garlic**, *Allium triquetrum*, make it a distinctive species. It has a small, whitish bulb, its leaves are mostly basal and its flowers hang in a one-sided umbel from the top of the flowering stem, 20–50cm (8–20in) tall. The flowers are bell-shaped, white with green lines on the midrib of each petal. This allium grows in damp, shady places, in woods and hedgerows, beside streams in Spain and France, and has been introduced into the Channel Islands and southwestern England. It is also found in a few places in south Wales and southern Ireland.

Ramsons
Allium ursinum

Triquetrous Garlic
Allium triquetrum

Field Garlic
Allium oleraceum

Crow Garlic
Allium vineale

Sand Leek
Allium scorodoprasum

Wild Daffodil
Narcissus pseudonarcissus

Snowdrop
Galanthus nivalis

Summer Snowflake
Leucojum aestivum

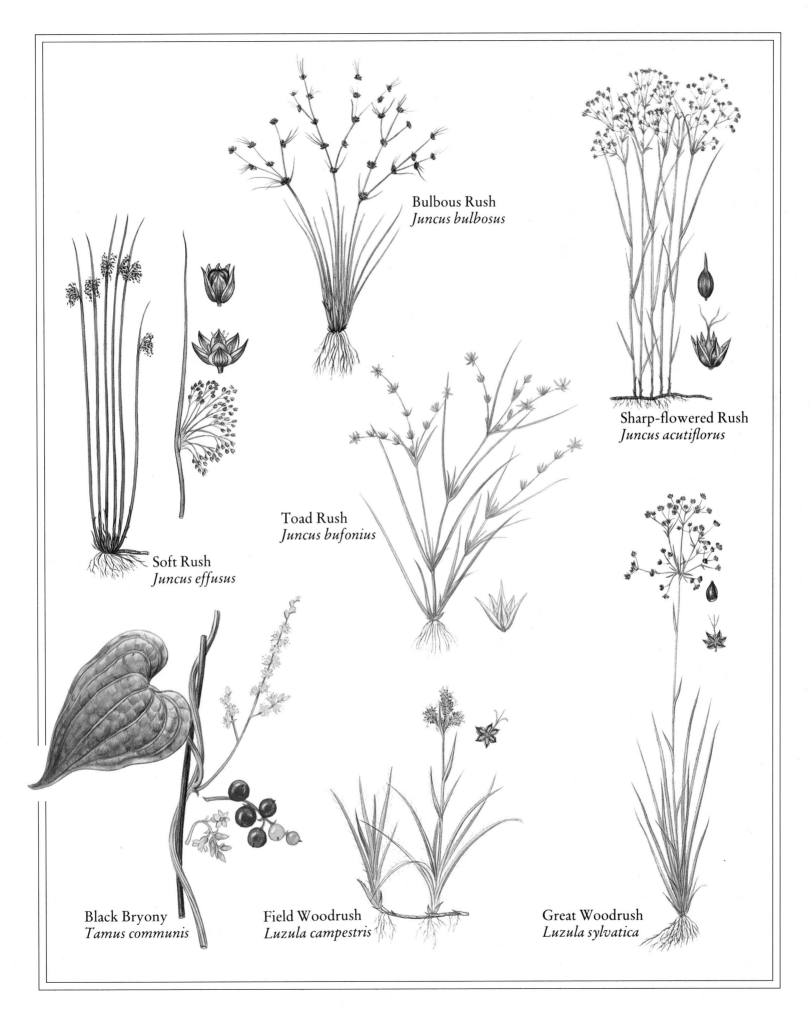

Bulbous Rush
Juncus bulbosus

Sharp-flowered Rush
Juncus acutiflorus

Soft Rush
Juncus effusus

Toad Rush
Juncus bufonius

Black Bryony
Tamus communis

Field Woodrush
Luzula campestris

Great Woodrush
Luzula sylvatica

Orchid family
Orchidaceae

This is one of the largest plant families, with about 735 genera and 17,000 species known to date; the figures increase every year as more are discovered and named. Many are found in temperate regions of the world, but far more grow in tropical jungles, and it is these jungle species which contribute most new species each year.

Family features Orchid flowers may be solitary, or borne in a spike, raceme or compound raceme. They are hermaphrodite and bilaterally symmetrical. Each flower has six perianth segments in two whorls; sometimes the two whorls are similar, but often they are unlike, the outer ones resembling sepals and the inner ones petals. Often there is one central sepal, which becomes the uppermost part of the flower, and two lateral sepals; and often there are two lateral petals, and a central one which becomes twisted to hang downwards, forming the lip or labellum. This latter structure is often complex and may be spurred, with nectar in the spur. The lateral sepals and petals often resemble each other. There are one or two stamens, their anthers borne together with the stigmas on a special structure known as the column. The pollen grains often adhere together to form small packets known as 'pollinia'. The ovary is inferior, usually with one cell. The fruit is usually a capsule containing numerous minute seeds (millions in some species). Orchids' leaves are entire and usually either arranged in two overlapping rows at the base of the stem or alternately on the stems; they are often fleshy with a sheathing base that encircles the stem, but they may be reduced to scales.

For many years horticulturalists failed to get orchid seeds to germinate. Finally it was realized that most orchids grow in a mycorrhizal association with a fungus. The fungus grows through and around the roots, and the orchid gets much of its water and nutrients from the fungus, not directly from the soil. Germinating orchid seeds have no food reserves and will die unless they connect with the right fungus very quickly.

There are about 50 **Lady's-slipper Orchids**, *Cypripedium* species, in the world but only three in Europe. Their name comes from the pouched lip of the flower, which is said to resemble a slipper; many of these beautiful orchids are now rare in the wild, their numbers reduced from overcollecting. **Yellow Lady's-slipper**, *C. calceolus*, has a creeping rhizome and an erect stem up to 45cm (18in) tall in early summer; this stem bears 3–4 large, elliptical leaves and one (sometimes two) flowers at the tip in the axil of a leafy bract. The flower is yellow and purple. It has wavy purple sepals, one erect at the top and the two lateral ones joined and pointing downwards, two purple, spirally twisted, linear lateral petals and a pale yellow pouched lip spotted with red on the inside. At one time this plant grew in woods and thickets, usually on calcareous

soils in hills and mountains, in many localities in Europe and in several places in northern England. It is now rare, eradicated in many of its former sites, with one small colony left in England.

Several Helleborines, *Epipactis* species, grow in Europe and the British Isles, some of them common (for orchids), others rare. **Marsh Helleborine**, *E. palustris*, is one of the more common ones, but its numbers are decreasing with the disappearance of its wetland habitats. It grows in fens and marshes, wet meadows and dune slacks locally across most of Europe, in England, Wales and Ireland. This is a perennial plant with a long-creeping rhizome, a slender, erect stem up to 45cm (18in) tall and several oblong to lance-shaped leaves, their bases clasping the stem; the lower part of the stem and the undersides of the lower leaves are often purplish. The flowers are borne in a terminal, more or less one-sided raceme, each one in the axil of a narrow, pointed bract. They have purplish-green sepals, hairy on the outside and paler on the inside, smaller whitish lateral petals veined with purple at their bases and a white lip veined with pink, spotted with yellow and frilly on the margin.

Broad-leaved Helleborine, *Epipactis helleborine*, has short rhizomes and one or more erect stems growing up to 80cm (30in) tall, with broadly ovate leaves, the largest in the middle of the stem and becoming smaller and narrower above and beneath. The flowers grow in one-sided, terminal racemes and vary in colour from dull purple to greenish; usually the sepals are greenish, the petals are purple and the heart-shaped lip may be purple or greenish-white, darker green or brown inside. This helleborine grows in woods and rocky places throughout Europe and the British Isles, but is rare in northern Scotland.

Dark Red Helleborine, *Epipactis atrorubens*, has a single erect stem about 30cm (1ft) tall, leafy with two rows of pointed-elliptical leaves. The flowers in the terminal raceme are red-purple and faintly scented. This plant grows among limestone rocks, in woods on calcareous soils, in grassy places and in dunes, locally across Europe, in north Wales and northern England, northern Scotland and western Ireland. Violet Helleborine, *E. purpurata*, has violet-tinged leaves and pale greenish-white flowers. This relatively rare plant grows in woods on calcareous soils in northern and central Europe, mainly in southern and central England in Britain.

The *Cephalanthera* species are also known as Helleborines. **White Helleborine**, *C. damasonium*, has a short, creeping rhizome and an erect, leafy stem up to 50cm (20in) tall. The leaves are ovate to lance-shaped, merging into leafy bracts near the top of the stem where the few flowers appear. These bracts are much larger than the flowers; the latter are creamy white, closed except for a brief time when they open into an up-facing bell, petals and sepals curved around the yellow-blotched lip. This plant grows in calcareous soils, in woods and shady places, scattered across Europe, mainly in southern England and the Midlands in Britain.

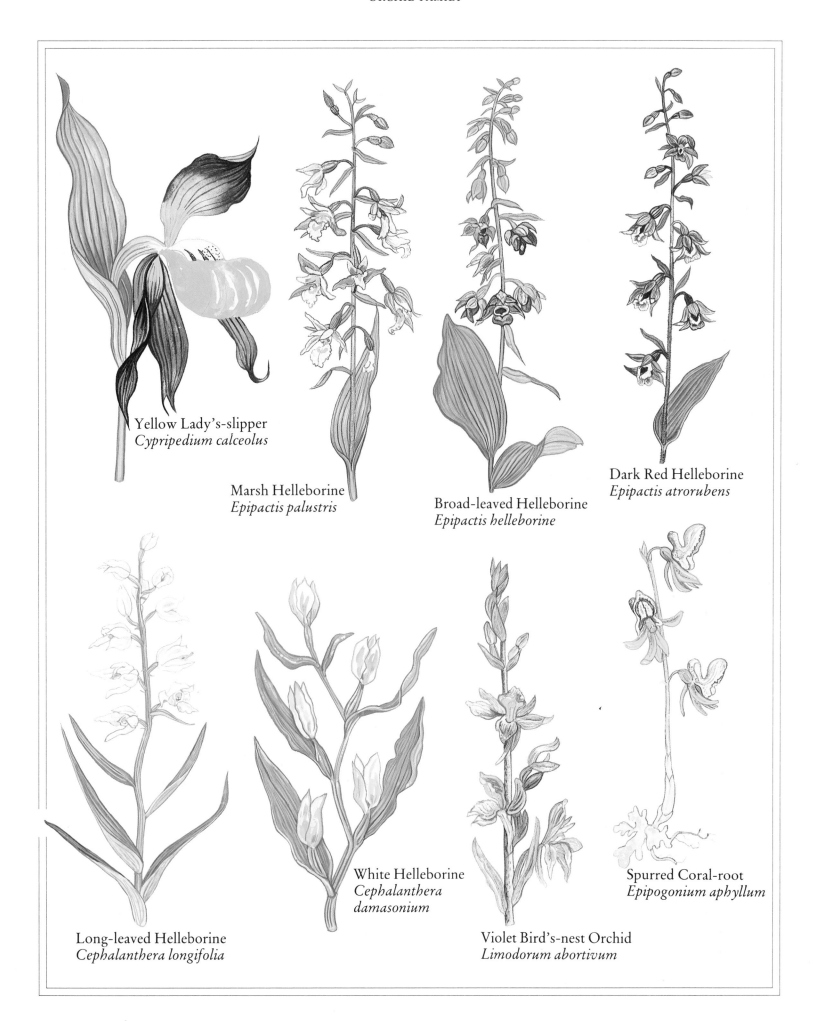

Yellow Lady's-slipper
Cypripedium calceolus

Marsh Helleborine
Epipactis palustris

Broad-leaved Helleborine
Epipactis helleborine

Dark Red Helleborine
Epipactis atrorubens

Long-leaved Helleborine
Cephalanthera longifolia

White Helleborine
*Cephalanthera
damasonium*

Violet Bird's-nest Orchid
Limodorum abortivum

Spurred Coral-root
Epipogonium aphyllum

Long-leaved Helleborine, *Cephalanthera longifolia* (p. 221), is similar but its leaves are lance-shaped, becoming linear higher up the stem, and its bracts are smaller than the flowers. This is a relatively rare and declining plant of woodland and scrub, especially fond of calcareous soils, scattered across southern and central Europe; it is found in only a few places in England, Scotland and Ireland.

Violet Bird's-nest Orchid, *Limodorum abortivum* (p. 221), is one of several unrelated orchids which have lost all or most of their chlorophyll, becoming saprophytic in their lifestyles. They usually grow in shady woods where there is a deep layer of leaf litter on the ground, and they depend on the mycorrhiza in their roots to absorb water and nutrients from this leafy humus. This species grows in woods across much of Europe, except the north, but is not found in the British Isles. Most of its life is spent underground, only the flowering stems appearing at unpredictable intervals. The upright stems grow up to 80cm (30in) tall, have several scale leaves and a terminal raceme of flowers, all violet in colour. The flowers have spreading lateral sepals and petals, a helmet-shaped upper sepal, a yellow-tinged lip and a downward-pointing spur.

Spurred Coral-root or Ghost Orchid, *Epipogonium aphyllum* (p. 221), is another saprophyte, a rare plant found in the deep shade of oak or beech woods, scattered across Europe, in a few places in England and Wales, sporadic and unpredictable in its appearance. It has no roots but its rhizome has many short, flattened branches, like a piece of whitish coral. Its flowering stem grows only 20cm (8in) tall and is translucent white tinged with pink and streaked with red, its leaves reduced to a few brownish sheaths around the swollen base. It has few flowers (sometimes only one) and they are unusual in that the lip is at the top with the petals and sepals hanging downwards below. The lip is large, spurred and three-lobed, white with violet spots; the petals and sepals are yellow.

Creeping Lady's Tresses, *Goodyera repens*, has creeping rhizomes beneath the surface of the ground and creeping stems above ending in rosettes of ovate leaves. These are mottled dark green with a network of conspicuous veins. The flowering stem grows from this rosette, reaching 25cm (10in) in height, bearing a spirally twisted raceme of creamy white, fragrant flowers in the latter half of summer. Each flower grows in the axil of a large linear bract which is green on the outside, white on the inside; the upper sepal and the two petals of each flower form a hood, the lateral sepals are spreading and the lip is flat and triangular. This rather rare orchid grows in mossy coniferous woodland in the hills and mountains across much of Europe; it is found locally in East Anglia and the north of England, more frequently in northern Scotland.

The Lady's Tresses, *Spiranthes* species, are small orchids with leafy, erect stems and characteristic, spirally twisted racemes of flowers. **Autumn Lady's Tresses**, *S. spiralis*, grows in damp, grassy places, in meadows and pastures, on sand-dunes and hills, usually in calcareous soils, throughout much of Europe, except the north, in England, Wales and Ireland, more commonly in the south. It has a rosette of ovate or elliptical leaves appearing in late summer and developing an erect flowering stem in late summer and autumn of the following year. By this time the leaves have withered but a new rosette has formed to one side. The flowering stem grows about 30cm (1ft tall), has overlapping scale leaves near the base and a single twisted row of scented, white flowers at the top.

Twayblade, *Listera ovata*, is a small orchid flowering in the early part of summer. It has a slender, erect flowering stem growing up to 60cm (2ft) tall, with a pair of rounded, opposite leaves towards the base. The flowers are small and spurless, yellow-green in colour and numerous, borne in a slender, spike-like raceme terminating the stem. The petals and sepals are joined at the base to form an open hood over the long, dangling lip; this has a deep notch at the tip. **Lesser Twayblade**, *L. cordata*, is a smaller, even more slender plant, with a flowering stem growing up to 20cm (8in) tall and fewer flowers in a shorter raceme. The two leaves are rounded with heart-shaped bases and the flowers are reddish, with an open hood and a forked, dangling lip.

Bird's-nest Orchid, *Neottia nidus-avis*, is another saprophytic species, growing only in shady woodland, particularly beneath beech, throughout much of Europe, Great Britain and Ireland, most commonly in the south. The name of this plant refers to the ball of thick, fleshy roots which conceal the rhizome (the 'bird's nest'); this is buried in leaf litter on the woodland floor and the plant only appears above ground when it flowers. It has a stiff, erect flowering stem reaching 45cm (18in) tall, brownish in colour with many membranous, brown scale leaves and ending in a dense spike of many brown flowers. Each one has its sepals and petals joined into an open hood, and a long, dangling, lobed lip, pouched at the base and often darker than the rest of the flower.

Coral-root, *Corallorhiza trifida* is partly saprophytic in its lifestyle, with a much-branched, fleshy, rounded rhizome resembling a piece of coral. It grows in damp, mossy woods, often beneath pine or alder, also in dune slacks, scattered across much of Europe, in northern England and Scotland, but is nevertheless a rare plant and its presence can only be detected when it flowers. Often several stems are produced, but this is a small orchid and they grow only 25cm (10in) tall at most. They are yellow-green in colour, with brown-veined, sheathing scale leaves near the base and a few inconspicuous flowers at the top. The sepals and lateral petals are similar in colour to the stems, but the lip is whitish and spotted with crimson.

Fen Orchid, *Liparis loeselii*, is more nearly related to the tropical orchids than most British species, the relationship demonstrated by the way the base of the stem is swollen to form a structure known as a pseudo-bulb, a feature seen in many tropical species. Fen Orchid is a small plant with an erect

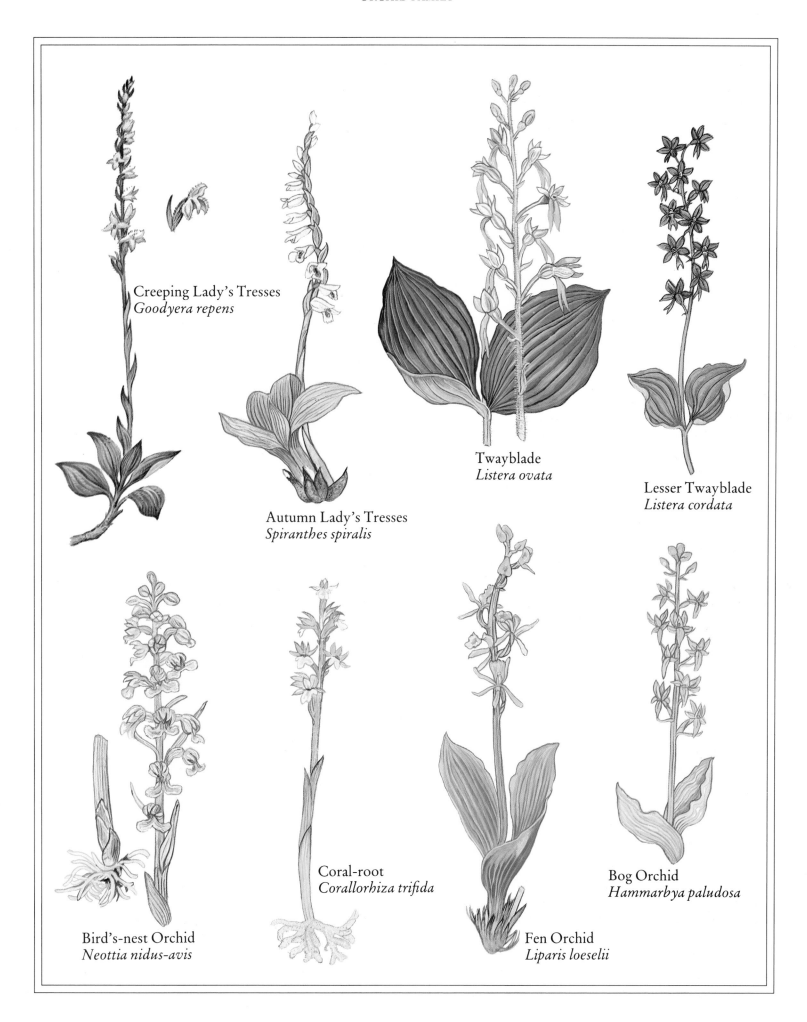

Creeping Lady's Tresses
Goodyera repens

Autumn Lady's Tresses
Spiranthes spiralis

Twayblade
Listera ovata

Lesser Twayblade
Listera cordata

Bird's-nest Orchid
Neottia nidus-avis

Coral-root
Corallorhiza trifida

Fen Orchid
Liparis loeselii

Bog Orchid
Hammarbya paludosa

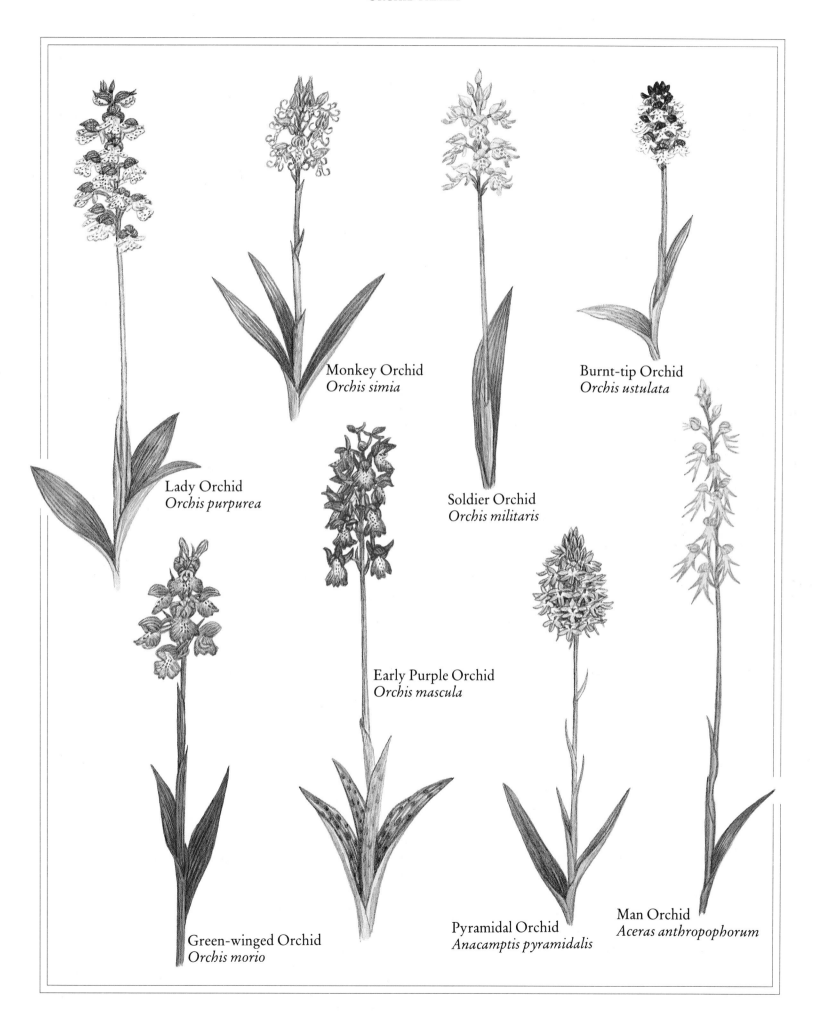

Monkey Orchid
Orchis simia

Burnt-tip Orchid
Orchis ustulata

Lady Orchid
Orchis purpurea

Soldier Orchid
Orchis militaris

Early Purple Orchid
Orchis mascula

Green-winged Orchid
Orchis morio

Pyramidal Orchid
Anacamptis pyramidalis

Man Orchid
Aceras anthropophorum

Arum family
Araceae

A family of herbaceous plants, with about 115 genera and 2000 species mainly from the tropics. Tropical species often come from damp and steamy jungles, while more temperate species are frequently found in wet places. Several popular house plants come from this family, mostly grown for their large and impressive leaves rather than for their curious flowers. They include philodendrons, dieffenbachias and monsteras. Garden species include arums and calla lilies. Many of the plants in this family contain poisonous juice; however, they rarely cause serious poisoning because the juice is so acrid that it burns the lips and mouth, and is therefore not swallowed.

Family features The flowers are very small, often with an offensive scent, and borne in a dense spike (a spadix), usually subtended by a leafy bract (a spathe). The flowers may be hermaphrodite or unisexual; if unisexual, then the male flowers are borne on the upper part of the spadix, the females below. Hermaphrodite flowers usually have a perianth, with 4–6 lobes, free or forming a cup, but this is absent in unisexual flowers. There are 2–8 stamens opposite the perianth segments. The ovary is superior or embedded in the spadix and has 1–3 cells. The fruit is usually a berry, but may be leathery and split open. The leaves often have sheathing bases; they usually form a basal clump growing directly from the rhizome. The plants have watery or milky, acrid juice.

Sweetflag, *Acorus calamus*, is found in shallow water on the margins of slow-moving rivers and canals, ponds and lakes across much of Europe, except the north, mainly in England in the British Isles; it has been introduced from Asia. It spreads by stout rhizomes that creep in the mud, forming colonies of sword-like, wavy-edged leaves up to 1m (3ft) tall. The leaves have a scent of tangerines and cinnamon when bruised. Stems that look like three-angled leaves also grow from the rhizomes to bear flower spikes about halfway up, growing at an angle of about 45 degrees to the stems. The spikes bear densely packed, yellowish, hermaphrodite flowers with an unpleasant scent. Sweetflag rhizomes yield a volatile oil known as Calamus Oil, used in perfumery; the rhizomes are also used in herb medicine and in the production of Stockton Bitters. In medieval times the leaves were strewn as rushes on the floors of churches, castles and manor houses for their sweet scent.

Cuckoo-pint or Lords-and-ladies, *Arum maculatum*, is one of those plants with a multitude of names and much folklore, a lot of it sexual in nature (perhaps inevitably, given the appearance of its flowers). It grows in hedgerows and woods across much of Europe, except the north, and throughout England, Wales and Ireland, less frequently in Scotland. The large leaves unfurl in spring; they are shiny green, often black-spotted, arrow-shaped with long stalks. They are followed by the spathe, pale yellow-green and edged or streaked with purple, containing the dull purple spadix. Once the flowers are pollinated the spathe and leaves gradually wither, leaving the cluster of green berries at the top of a bare stalk; these gradually turn red as they ripen in late summer. They are very poisonous and the whole plant contains acrid, irritant sap.

Duckweed family
Lemnaceae

A small family of floating aquatic plants, with 3 genera and about 40 species, found in fresh water throughout the world.

The **Duckweeds**, the *Lemna* species, are found in the still waters of ponds and ditches. They have floating, leaf-like fronds (known as the 'thallus') and minute flowers which lack petals or sepals. **Common Duckweed**, *L. minor*, has opaque, rounded thalli which constantly divide into new ones; these may remain attached to the original thallus, or split off and float away. Each thallus has a single root beneath and may form flowers, which are developed in a cavity on the upper surface; flowers usually appear only in plants growing in shallow water in full sunlight. This is easily the most common species, growing in ponds and ditches (often covering the whole surface by late summer) throughout Europe, much of Great Britain and Ireland, becoming rare in northern Scotland.

Ivy-leaved Duckweed, *Lemna trisulca*, is a submerged species floating just beneath the surface of the water in ponds and ditches throughout Europe and much of the British Isles, but rare in Scotland and in the west. Its thalli are translucent and pointed-oval in shape; they float in clumps, several thalli joined together by their stalks, new ones arising in opposite pairs and at right angles to the parent.

Bulrush family
Typhaceae

A very small family, with only one genus, *Typha*, and 10 species, found throughout the world. All are aquatic plants, growing in shallow water, in marshes and reed-beds, along the edges of ponds and slow-moving rivers, and in ditches.

They are tall, perennial plants with creeping rhizomes, forming wide colonies in the right conditions—in marshes, for instance, where shallow water covers mud. Such places form excellent hiding and nesting places for aquatic birds. The erect stems grow up to 2.5m (9ft) tall in the largest species, with thick, sword-like leaves growing from the bases of the stems in overlapping rows. The stems are stiff and unbranched and bear the flowers in distinctive, terminal, cylindrical heads, the

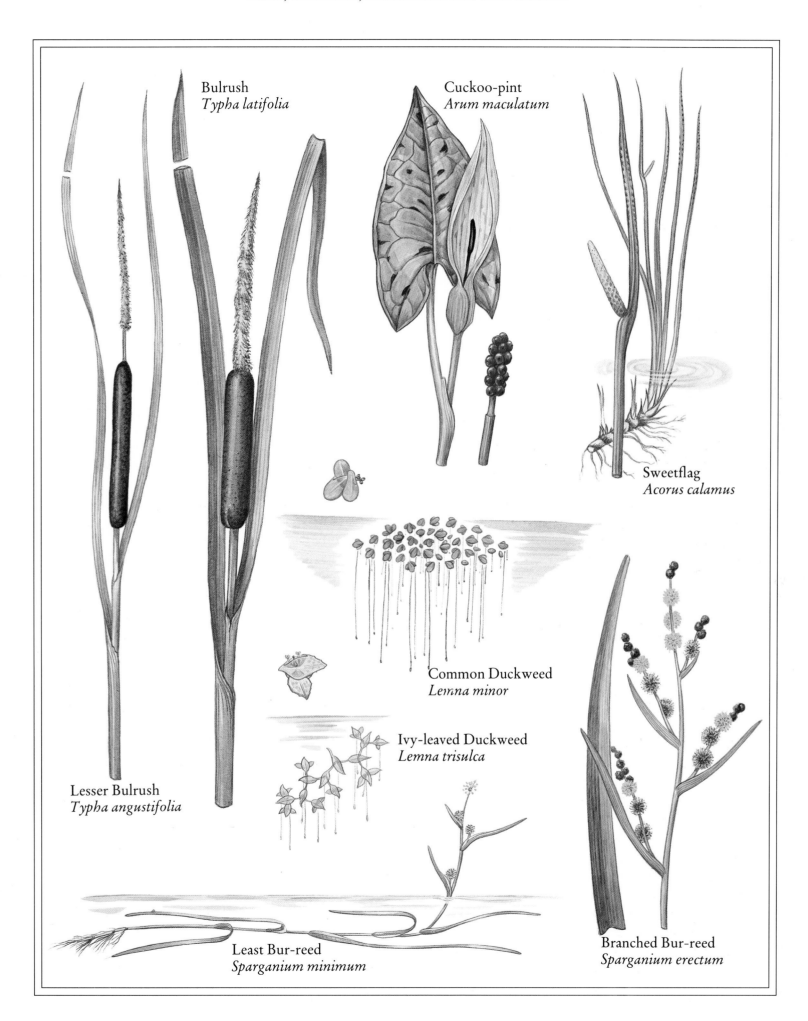

Bulrush
Typha latifolia

Cuckoo-pint
Arum maculatum

Sweetflag
Acorus calamus

Lesser Bulrush
Typha angustifolia

Common Duckweed
Lemna minor

Ivy-leaved Duckweed
Lemna trisulca

Branched Bur-reed
Sparganium erectum

Least Bur-reed
Sparganium minimum

greenish female flowers below and the male flowers above, yellow with pollen when in full bloom. The male flowers are shed after the pollen has blown away to pollinate the females, leaving a bare stalk, but the female flowers go on to form the brown fruiting heads. These are more familiar, as they last for months, persisting into autumn and winter.

Bulrush, *Typha latifolia* (p. 231), is the largest, growing up to 2.4m (9ft) tall, with leaves up to 20mm ($^3/_4$in) across. Its male and female flowers form one continuous cylindrical flower spike. It is also known as Cat's-tail and Greater Reedmace. The **Lesser Bulrush** or Lesser Reedmace, *T. angustifolia* (p. 231), is smaller, usually not more than 2m (6ft) tall, with narrow leaves only 6mm ($^1/_4$in) wide. Its male and female flowers are separated by a section of stem up to 8cm (3in) long. Both species are widespread in Europe north to southern Scandinavia, but the Bulrush is common while the Lesser Bulrush is much rarer. In the British Isles Bulrushes are common in England, Wales and Ireland, rare in Scotland; Lesser Bulrushes are scattered in England, rare in other areas.

Bur-reed family
Sparganiaceae

A small family of aquatic plants, with only one genus and about 20 species, but found in many parts of the world.

The **Bur-reeds**, *Sparganium* species, are perennial plants which spread by creeping rhizomes in marshes, or in shallow water on the edges of ponds and slow-moving rivers; they may form extensive stands. They have erect or floating stems and narrow, grass-like leaves, the bases of the leaves sheathing the stems. Their flowers are borne in small green balls, male flowers near the tip of the stem, female ones below.

Branched Bur-reed, *Sparganium erectum* (p. 231), varies in height, often 30–60cm (1–2ft) but sometimes up to 2m (6ft) tall. It has clumps of erect, three-angled leaves and branched flowering stems in the latter half of summer, the balls of male flowers borne above the females on the branches. Unbranched Bur-reed, *S. emersum*, has unbranched flowering stems and some of its leaves are floating. Both bur-reeds grow in shallow water throughout much of Europe and the British Isles, becoming much less common in the north. Branched Bur-reed is common in ponds, slow-moving rivers and ditches and in marshes; Unbranched Bur-reed is less common, growing on the margins of ponds and lakes.

Least Bur-reed, *Sparganium minimum* (p. 231), is a floating species, its stems and translucent, ribbon-like leaves floating on the surface of lakes, ponds and ditches in many areas of Europe and much of the British Isles; it is rare in the south. It is a small plant, its stems growing 30cm (1ft) long at most; its flowers are borne on stems emerging from the water, the females in balls on the stem, the males on stalks.

Sedge family
Cyperaceae

A large family of herbaceous plants, with about 100 genera and 4000 species, found throughout the world. Many are inconspicuous plants which go unnoticed among the grasses and they are of little economic importance. Papyrus, used as paper in ancient Egypt, came from a member of this family.

Family features The flowers are very small and inconspicuous; they may be hermaphrodite or unisexual and are arranged in small spikes (known as spikelets), each one solitary in the axil of a special bract called a glume. The spikelets are gathered into flower spikes and within these the glumes may be spirally arranged or borne in two opposite rows. In each flower there may be a perianth formed of scales or hairs, or the perianth may be absent; there are usually 2–3 stamens and a superior, single-celled ovary with two or three styles. The fruits are indehiscent nutlets. These plants often have rhizomes. Their leaves are basal or crowded at the bottom of the stem, linear in shape with a sheathing base and a narrow blade, or the blade may be absent.

The **Cotton-grasses**, *Eriophorum* species, are often the most conspicuous plants in their landscape (unlike most members of this family). About 20 species grow in fens and bogs, or on wet moors, in northern temperate and Arctic regions of the world. **Common Cotton-grass**, *E. angustifolium*, has creeping rhizomes and forms extensive colonies, with broadly linear, channelled leaves. The plants flower in early summer, the flower spikes borne in umbels at the tops of slender stems; the white cottony tufts of hairs that are such a conspicuous feature of this plant appear with the fruits and remain through the summer. It grows in wet bogs and fens across most of Europe and throughout the British Isles, much more commonly in the north, disappearing with improved drainage in many southern areas. Cotton-grass or Hare's-tail, *E. vaginatum*, is also common in the north; this species forms leafy tussocks and has a single tuft of white perched at the top of each stem.

Deer-grass, *Trichophorum cespitosum* (for many years *Scirpus caespitosus*), grows in damp upland heaths and moors, especially in blanket bogs, forming tussocks of slender stems. It is found throughout most of Europe and much of the British Isles, much more widespread and common in the north than in the south, and absent from parts of central England. It is a small plant, only 25cm (10in) tall at most, and its smooth stems are almost leafless, the leaves replaced by brownish sheaths at the base of the stem; only the uppermost sheath has a tiny blade. At the tip of each stem is a solitary, pale brown spikelet.

The **Spike-rushes**, *Eleocharis* species, are similar in form to Deer-grass, but in these species the uppermost sheath on the stem lacks a blade. **Common Spike-rush**, *E. palustris*, has far-creeping rhizomes and single stems or small tufts of stems

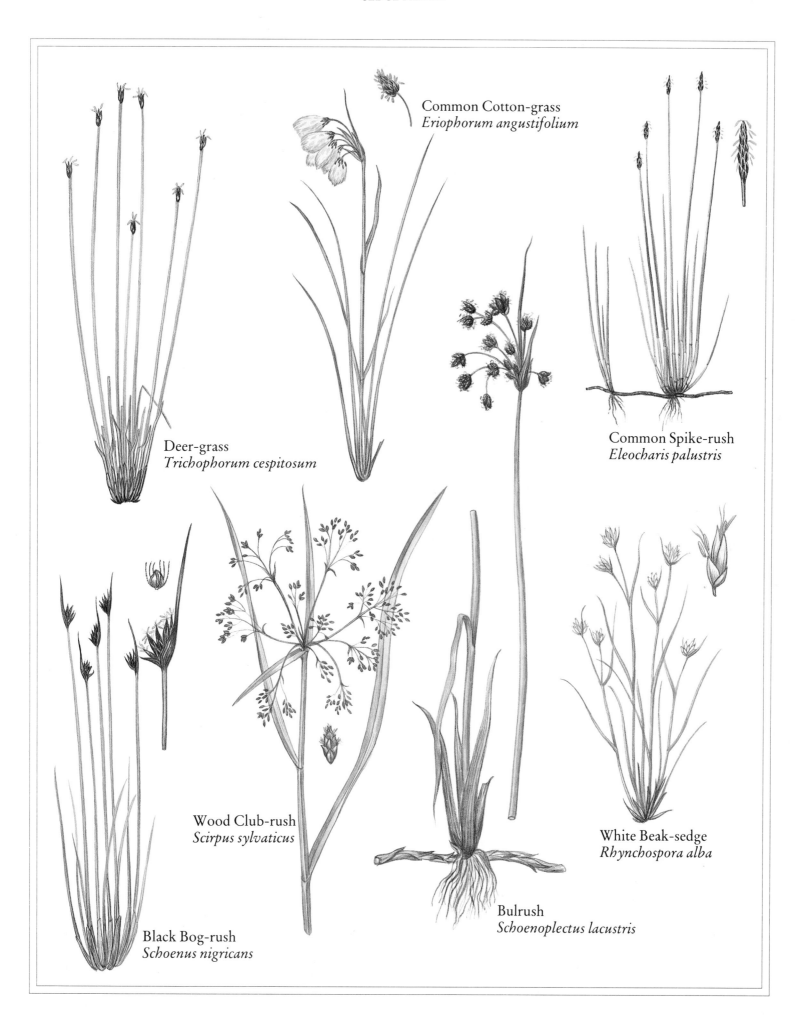

Common Cotton-grass
Eriophorum angustifolium

Deer-grass
Trichophorum cespitosum

Common Spike-rush
Eleocharis palustris

Wood Club-rush
Scirpus sylvaticus

White Beak-sedge
Rhynchospora alba

Black Bog-rush
Schoenus nigricans

Bulrush
Schoenoplectus lacustris

which may grow 60cm (2ft) tall, reddish at the base and with no blades on any of its yellow-brown sheaths. Solitary spikes of brown flowers tip the stems, the two lowest glumes sterile and much shorter than the spikelet. Plants grow in marshes and wet meadows, at the margins of lakes and ponds, and in ditches throughout Europe and the British Isles.

The **Club-rushes**, *Scirpus* species, are perennial plants with leafy stems and much-branched, terminal inflorescences. About 15 are found in Europe. **Wood Club-rush**, *S. sylvaticus* (p. 233), grows in wet places in woods and in marshes throughout most of Europe; it is scattered across the British Isles, but absent from northern Scotland and much of Ireland. This is a tall plant, with stout, erect, three-angled stems up to 120cm (4ft) in height, many broad, flat leaves with rough margins, and branched clusters of numerous greenish-brown spikelets in summer. Sea Club-rush, *S. maritimus*, is similar but smaller, with narrower leaves and red-brown spikelets. It grows in ditches and ponds near the sea and in tidal estuaries around the coast of Europe and the British Isles.

Black Bog-rush, *Schoenus nigricans* (p. 233), forms dense perennial tufts of wiry stems and leaves up to 75cm (30in) tall in marshes and other damp, peaty places, particularly near the sea, in most of Europe and the British Isles; it is much more common in Scotland and Ireland than in England or Wales. The leaves are cylindrical with inrolled margins, growing as tall as the stems, and the tips of the stems bear dense tufts of blackish flowers in early summer.

White Beak-sedge, *Rhynchospora alba* (p. 233), grows in bogs and marshes, in peaty, acid soils, scattered across Europe and the British Isles, mainly in the north and west. It is a tufted perennial, its stems slender and growing up to 50cm (20in) tall, its shorter, channelled leaves growing from the bases of the stems. The lowermost sheaths produce no leaves, but often have bulbils in their axils. In summer the distinctive whitish spikelets are borne in dense clusters at the tips of the stems, often with one or two lateral clusters as well, all of them on long stalks in the axils of leaf-like bracts.

Bulrushes, *Schoenoplectus lacustris* (p. 233), are familiar to many people, not as living plants but as the rushes with which mats, baskets and chair-seats are made; they are also used for thatching. The plant is ideal for this kind of use, since the stems grow straight and up to 3m (9ft) long, they are flexible and they have a natural waterproofing (from growing in wet places). Bulrushes grow in ponds and lakes, usually when they are silting up, across Europe and scattered throughout the British Isles. They have creeping rhizomes, round stems with the lowermost leaves linear and submerged, upper ones reduced to sheaths. The plants flower in summer, producing dense clusters of reddish-brown spikelets at the tops of the stems.

The true **Sedges** are a huge group, with about 2000 species in the genus *Carex*, found throughout the world; about 160 grow wild in Europe. They have solid, three-angled stems and linear, often keeled leaves. The flowers are unisexual, borne in one-flowered spikelets, each with a glume; the spikelets are gathered into several spikes, often male flowers in the terminal spike(s) and females in the lower one(s).

Sand Sedge, *Carex arenaria*, spreads rapidly with its far-creeping rhizomes, helping to stabilize sand-dunes around the coasts of the British Isles and Europe. It often grows in straight lines, marked by tufts of rigid leaves with inrolled margins. The erect flowering stems appear in summer, growing up to 40cm (15in) tall, with several dense, terminal flower spikes, male flowers in the upper spikes, mixed flowers in the middle and female flowers in the lower ones.

The **Flea Sedge**, *Carex pulicaris*, is unusual among sedges in having a solitary, terminal flower spike, with a cluster of male flowers above and females below. The female flowers are erect at first, spreading and drooping as the spindle-shaped fruits ripen and soon losing their reddish-brown glumes. This is a small but creeping plant, forming dense patches of narrow channelled leaves and slender stems only 30cm (1ft) tall at most. It grows in damp, calcareous grassland, base-rich fens and moors across most of Europe and the British Isles, but is uncommon in the south and east.

The **Hairy Sedge**, *Carex hirta*, grows in woods and rough grassland, in damp meadows, on roadsides and in hedgerows throughout Europe and much of the British Isles, becoming rare in Scotland. It is typical of many sedges in that the male and female flower spikes are quite separate, the female spikes lower down the stem and the males at the top. In this species there are 2–3 widely spaced, green, female spikes, the lowest often near the base of the stem, and 2–3 erect, reddish-brown male spikes at the top. This sedge is readily recognizable from its hairy leaves and shaggy leaf sheaths, and from its hairy fruits. It is a perennial, with tufts of leafy stems about 15–60cm (6–24in) tall.

Carnation Sedge, *Carex panicea*, grows in wet places like many other sedges, this species in fens and marshes, in wet, grassy places and mountain moors across much of Europe and throughout the British Isles, becoming less common in the south. It is a tufted perennial plant, with bluish or greyish leaves (like those of carnations) and erect stems up to 60cm (2ft) tall, flowering in summer. The female spikes are erect, solitary or widely spaced with few flowers, the single male spike brown. The fruits are distinctive—inflated and egg-shaped, smooth and grey-green, often purple-tinged.

Spring Sedge, *Carex caryophyllea*, is one of the smallest sedges, a perennial with tufts of leaves and slender stems often only 5–15cm (2–6in) tall, growing from short, creeping rhizomes. It has a single brown, club-shaped male spike at the top of each stem and 1–3 touching female spikes below, followed by olive-green, three-angled fruits. The tufts of leaves remain green in winter and the plants flower in spring; they grow in dry grassland, usually on calcareous or base-rich soils,

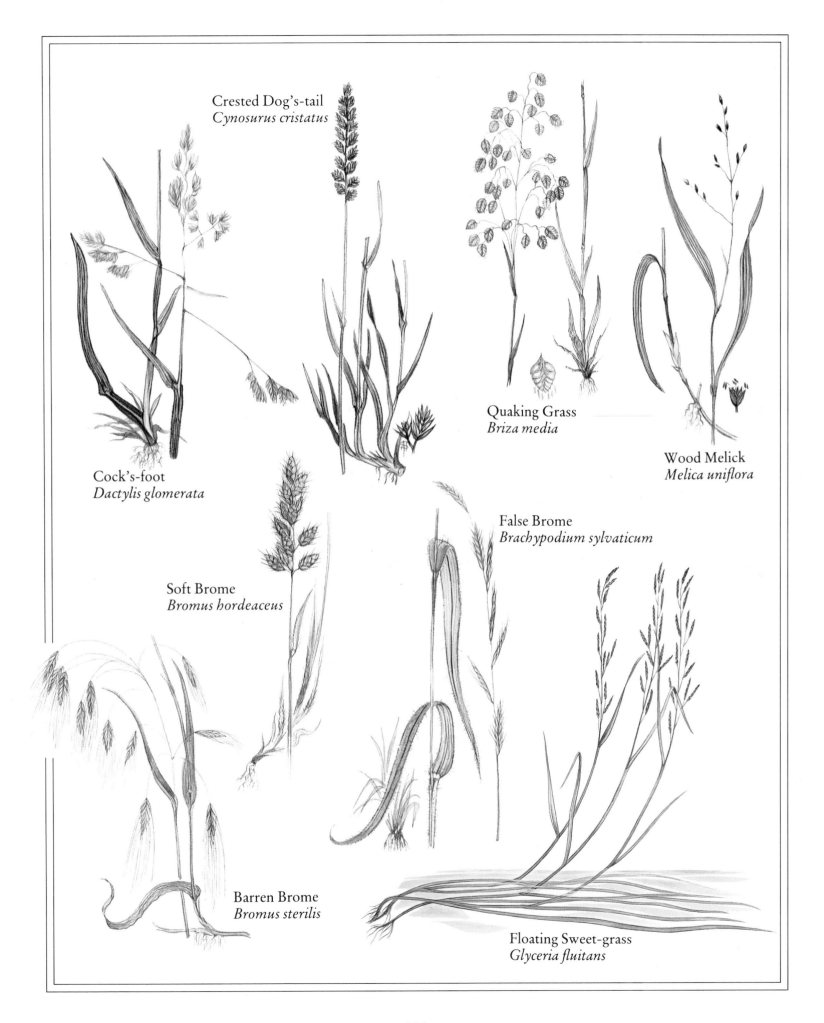

Crested Dog's-tail
Cynosurus cristatus

Cock's-foot
Dactylis glomerata

Quaking Grass
Briza media

Wood Melick
Melica uniflora

Soft Brome
Bromus hordeaceus

False Brome
Brachypodium sylvaticum

Barren Brome
Bromus sterilis

Floating Sweet-grass
Glyceria fluitans

ing inflorescence. Quaking Grass grows in a variety of grassy places, often in calcareous soils. It is found across much of Europe and the British Isles, becoming rare or absent in northern and western Scotland.

Wood Melick, *Melica uniflora* (p. 239), is one of the few plants to grow in beech woods, in clearings and rides, also more generally in woodland margins and shady hedgerows. It is found throughout most of Europe and the British Isles, less commonly in Ireland and Scotland. This is another attractive grass with a delicate inflorescence. It is a perennial, with creeping rhizomes and bright green, flat leaves, rough on their undersides and with long hairs on their upper surfaces. In early summer the flowering stems grow about 60cm (2ft) tall, ending in branched, arching inflorescences with erect spikelets; each spikelet contains only two florets, one fertile and the other sterile, cupped in two purplish-brown glumes.

The **Brome Grasses** are a group of about 50 species in the genus *Bromus*, found mostly in northern temperate areas; about 35 grow in Europe. They may be annuals, biennials or perennials; they have flat leaves and flattened spikelets formed of numerous overlapping florets. The glumes are unequal —usually the upper one is the larger of the two. In many species the florets have long awns.

Barren Brome, *Bromus sterilis* (p. 239), is an untidy annual plant with soft, downy leaves and sprawling, hairless stems growing up to 1m (3ft) tall. In summer the inflorescence droops with the weight of its flattened, long-awned spikelets, one spikelet to each branch. This is a common grass, growing in waste places and beside roads, on the margins of fields and as a garden weed throughout Europe and much of Great Britain, but absent from much of Scotland and scattered in Ireland.

Soft Brome or Lop-grass, *Bromus hordeaceus* (p. 239), also has awned spikelets but in this species the awns are much shorter. This plant may be annual or biennial; it has soft, often hairy leaves, and flowers in summer, with a flowering stem up to 80cm (30in) tall and an erect, dense inflorescence of hairy, short-awned spikelets. It grows in grassy places, meadows, on roadsides and waste ground, often in sand-dunes and on cliffs beside the sea, throughout Europe and the British Isles; however, it is much more common in the south than the north.

False Brome, *Brachypodium sylvaticum* (p. 239), is a woodland grass found in woods and hedgerows, sometimes in grassland where a wood once existed, throughout Europe and the British Isles. It is a perennial, with broad, yellow-green, drooping leaves, rough to the touch, erect flowering stems up to 90cm (3ft) tall and slender, nodding inflorescences formed of alternate spikelets. These are so narrow as to be almost linear in shape, finely awned and borne on short stalks.

The **Couch Grasses** are a large group of about 100 species, many of them until recently placed in the genus *Agropyron*, but now moved to *Elymus*. They are tough perennial plants, usually with creeping rhizomes and narrow, zigzag flowering spikes, the spikelets arranged broadside on to the stem. **Couch Grass** or Twitch, *E. repens*, is a notorious garden weed, extremely difficult to eradicate, invading and taking over lawns, vegetable gardens and flower beds if left unchecked. It also grows on roadsides and in waste places, in arable land and rough grassland throughout Europe and the British Isles. It has many prostrate non-flowering shoots and erect flowering stems up to 120cm (4ft) tall, with dull green leaves and zigzag spikes of overlapping spikelets. The similar Sea Couch Grass, *E. pycnanthus*, is a coastal species found in sand-dunes and on sandy shores; its stems and leaves are stiff and rigid, and its leaves often have inrolled margins and pointed tips.

Lyme Grass, *Leymus arenarius* (formerly called *Elymus arenarius*), is a coastal plant found with Marram Grass on the shifting sands of sand-dunes (on the fore dunes, not in the relative safety of the fixed dunes), its creeping stems and ability to form new shoots when buried helping it to survive in this unstable environment and ultimately helping to bring stability. It is a stout perennial plant, forming large tufts of stems growing up to 2m (6ft) tall, with rigid, sharp-pointed, blue-grey leaves, their margins inrolled to cut down water loss. The plants flower in the latter half of summer, producing long, dense inflorescences with two spikelets at each node arranged in two rows alternating all along the stem. Each spikelet has two large glumes, often placed at the front of it.

Wild Oats, *Avena fatua*, are widespread in Europe, only common in southern and eastern England in Britain, scattered elsewhere, growing in arable land and waste places and flowering in late summer. This is an annual plant, growing up to 1m (3ft) tall, with a spreading inflorescence of dangling spikelets, silky-hairy in texture with tawny hairs and tipped with bent awns. The spikelets readily fall apart when the seeds are ripe. Cultivated Oats belong to a similar species.

Meadow Oat-grass, *Avenula pratensis* (formerly *Helictotrichon pratense*), grows in short grassland on chalk and limestone throughout western and central Europe and in Great Britain. It is a perennial plant with erect stems up to 80cm (30in) tall, stiff, grey-green, often channelled leaves, and a narrow inflorescence of large spikelets held erect on short branches. It flowers around midsummer. Downy Oat-grass, *A. pubescens*, has soft, downy leaves and a spreading inflorescence, with erect spikelets. It grows in rough grassland, on basic soils throughout the British Isles and Europe. In both these species the spikelets have long, abruptly bent awns.

False Oat-grass, *Arrhenatherum elatius*, is a robust, tufted perennial grass, with erect stems up to 50cm (20in) tall, sometimes swollen at the base. The leaves are flat and weak, often rough but with smooth sheaths. Plants flower in summer; the inflorescence is rather narrow but loose and often nodding, with several branches arising at every node and shiny, often purplish spikelets. Each spikelet has two florets, the upper one essentially awnless and the lemma of the lower one with a long,

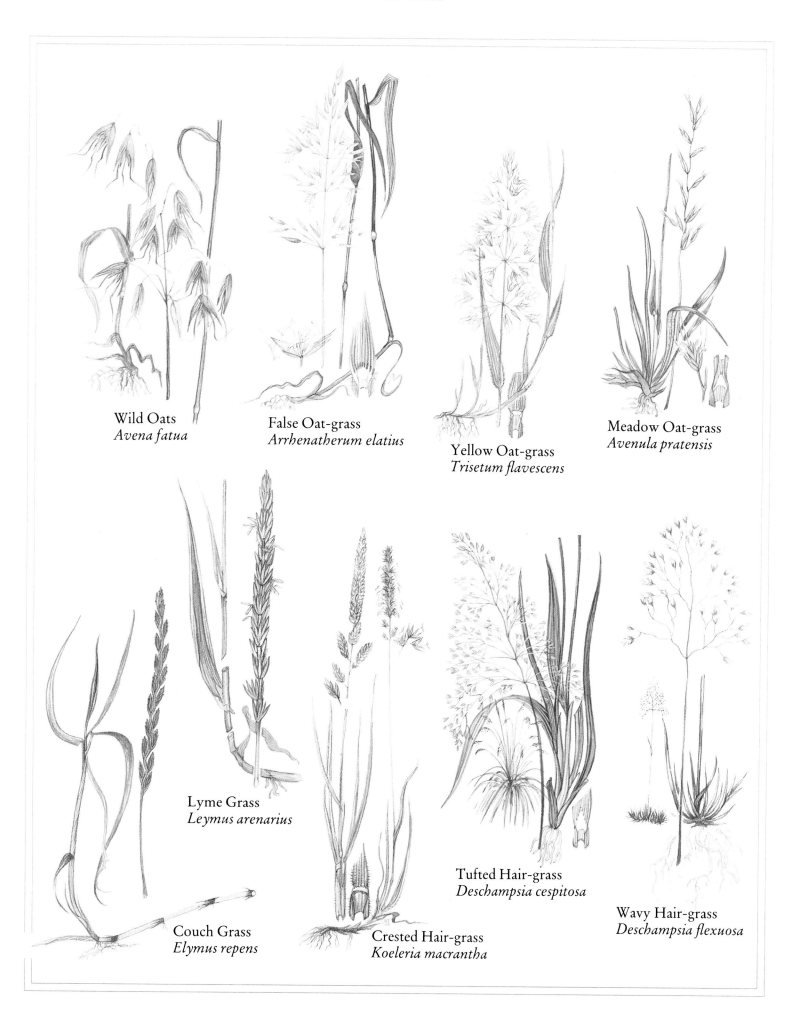

Wild Oats
Avena fatua

False Oat-grass
Arrhenatherum elatius

Yellow Oat-grass
Trisetum flavescens

Meadow Oat-grass
Avenula pratensis

Lyme Grass
Leymus arenarius

Couch Grass
Elymus repens

Crested Hair-grass
Koeleria macrantha

Tufted Hair-grass
Deschampsia cespitosa

Wavy Hair-grass
Deschampsia flexuosa

bent awn. This common grass grows in meadows, on rough, grassy roadsides, on waste ground, in scree and shingle throughout Europe and the British Isles.

Crested Hair-grass, *Koeleria macrantha* (p. 241), is another tufted perennial grass, this one found in short grassland on chalk and limestone scattered across much of Europe, except the north, and in many areas of the British Isles. It has tufts of narrow, flat or folded leaves with the old sheaths from last year persisting at the base, and erect stems up to 40cm (15in) tall, flowering in summer. The inflorescence is narrow and often lobed, formed of flattened, glistening spikelets, varying in colour from green to purplish.

Yellow Oat-grass, *Trisetum flavescens* (p. 241), gets its name from its numerous glistening, yellowish spikelets. It resembles Wild Oat in its appearance and in the bent awns on the spikelets, but the spikelets are much smaller and may be erect or nodding. Yellow Oat-grass is a loosely tufted perennial, with leaves softly hairy on their upper surface and erect flowering stems up to 80cm (30in) tall, flowering in early summer. It grows in meadows, pastures and other grassy places, especially in dry, calcareous soils, throughout Europe and much of the British Isles, but is absent from the north.

Tufted Hair-grass, *Deschampsia cespitosa* (p. 241), is one of about 10 species in this genus found in Europe, all stout, tufted perennial plants. It grows in damp meadows and woods, usually on heavy, poorly drained soils, also in marshes and wet moors, throughout Europe and the British Isles. This may be a large plant, with dense tussocks of coarse leaves and stiff stems up to 2m (6ft) in height. It flowers in the latter half of summer, with lax, nodding inflorescences of numerous spikelets on slender stems; these spikelets are shiny, often silvery or purplish in colour, with straight awns.

Wavy Hair-grass, *Deschampsia flexuosa* (p. 241), is a smaller, more slender but also densely tufted plant, which has bristle-like, rough-edged leaves and stems up to 1m (3ft) tall. It flowers around midsummer, forming a delicate inflorescence with long, wavy branches and shiny spikelets, often silvery or purplish with bent awns. This grass grows in acid soils, in poor grassland, on dry moors, heaths and in open woods throughout Europe and the British Isles. It is often the only plant that can grow in the acid 'soil' of colliery spoil tips.

Sweet Vernal Grass, *Anthoxanthum odoratum*, gets its name from its scent of coumarin, more familiar to most people as the smell of new-mown hay (which actually gets its scent from Sweet Vernal Grass). It grows in meadows and pastures, heaths and moors, and in open woodland throughout Europe and the British Isles. This is a tufted perennial grass, with short flat, somewhat hairy leaves, and flowering stems up to 50cm (20in) tall. It flowers in spring and early summer, producing spike-like inflorescences of green spikelets with bent awns.

Yorkshire Fog, *Holcus lanatus*, is an apt name for this plant, with its soft leaves and grey-purple flowers. It is a tufted, short-lived perennial grass found on roadsides and waste places, in woods, fields and meadows throughout Europe and the British Isles. It has flat, softly downy leaves, flowering stems up to 1m (3ft) tall in summer and bushy inflorescences, starting out dense and then opening up, varying in colour from whitish to pinkish-green or purple, attractive to the sight and touch. The spikelets have hooked awns.

Creeping Soft-grass, *Holcus mollis*, is a true perennial plant, with creeping rhizomes and tufts or mats of rough leaves. It flowers around midsummer, with stiff, erect flowering stems up to 1m (3ft) tall, their joints conspicuously hairy, and branched inflorescences of brownish or purplish spikelets with bent awns. This grass grows in acid soils, usually in woodland but also on heaths and in pastures, throughout Europe and the British Isles.

The **Bent-grasses** are a large group of about 200 species in the genus *Agrostis*, found in temperate regions of the world. They are tufted or creeping perennial plants with small spikelets, each spikelet containing only one floret. **Brown Bent-grass**, *A. canina*, grows in damp, grassy places in acid soils, one of several common *Agrostis* species found throughout Europe and the British Isles. It forms loose tufts of stems with flat leaves, up to 60cm (2ft) tall, some of the stems sprawling and rooting at the nodes, others erect. It flowers around midsummer, producing purplish-brown inflorescences that are compact before and after flowering, loosely branched while the flowers are open.

Marram Grass, *Ammophila arenaria*, is the most obvious of the sand-dune grasses, forming large, untidy clumps on the fore dunes all around the coasts of western Europe and the British Isles. It spreads by means of far-creeping rhizomes, rooting at the nodes and producing new plants, penetrating through the sand and gradually stabilizing it until other plants can also begin to colonize the dunes. Its leaves are distinctive, long and narrow with sharp points, rolled almost into a cylinder, smooth and polished on the outside, ribbed on the inside, superbly adapted for conserving water. Marram Grass flowers in the latter half of summer, producing erect stems up to 120cm (4ft) tall and dense, cylindrical inflorescences of whitish, one-flowered spikelets.

The **Small-reeds**, *Calamagrostis* species, are a large group of about 280 tall, perennial grasses found in damp places in the temperate regions of the world; about 20 grow in Europe, together with their hybrids. **Wood Small-reed** or Bushgrass, *C. epigejos*, forms dense patches of stout, erect stems up to 2m (6ft) tall in damp woods and fens, in ditches and beside streams across most of Europe and in England; it is found more rarely in Wales and Scotland. It has flat, long-pointed, rough leaves and branched, spreading inflorescences of purple-brown spikelets in the latter half of summer. Each spikelet contains only one floret with numerous silky hairs at its base (this is true for all small-reeds).

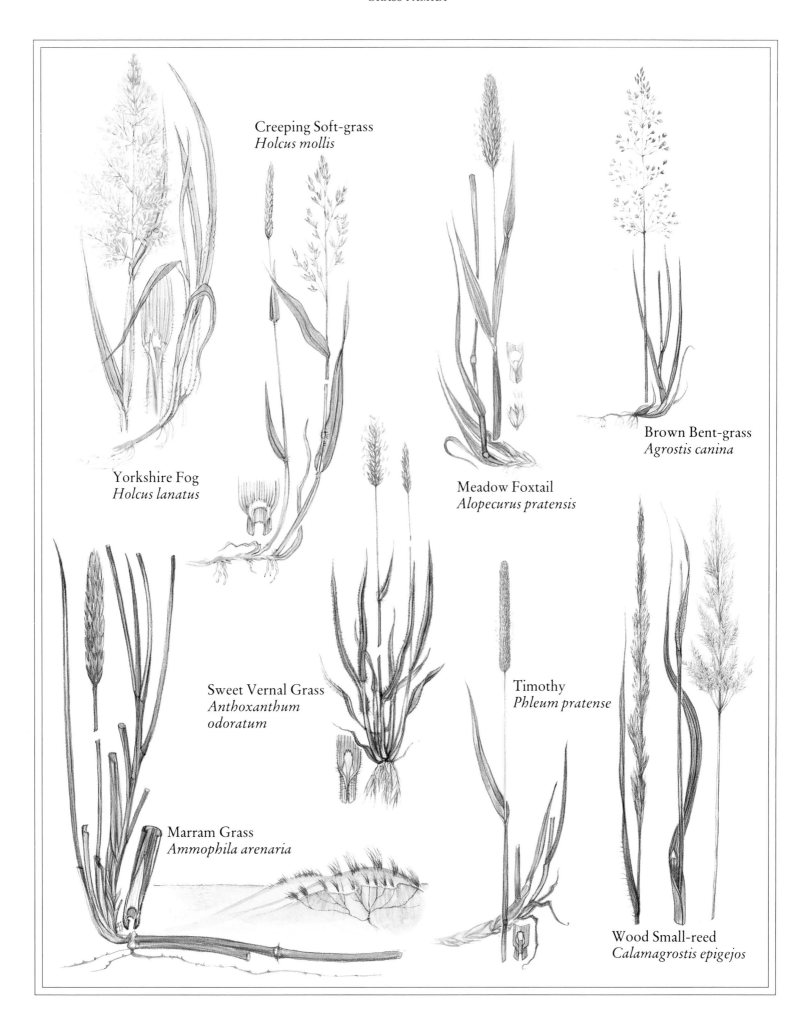

Creeping Soft-grass
Holcus mollis

Brown Bent-grass
Agrostis canina

Yorkshire Fog
Holcus lanatus

Meadow Foxtail
Alopecurus pratensis

Sweet Vernal Grass
*Anthoxanthum
odoratum*

Timothy
Phleum pratense

Marram Grass
Ammophila arenaria

Wood Small-reed
Calamagrostis epigejos

Garden (*L. sativa*) 198
  Prickly (*L. serriola*) 198, **199**
Lettuce, Wall (*Mycelis muralis*) 198, **199**
Liquorice (*Glycyrrhiza glabra*) 72, **73**
  Wild (*Astragalus glycyphyllos*) 72, **73**
Lilac, French 72
Lilies (*Lilium* spp.) 208
  Martagon (*L. martagon*) **209**, 210
Lily family (Liliaceae) 206
Lily, Loddon 214
  May (*Maianthemum bifolium*) **207**, 208
  Snowdon (*Lloydia serotina*) **209**, 210
Lily-of-the-valley (*Convallaria majalis*) **207**, 208
Ling 114
Lobelias (*Lobelia* spp.) 170
  Heath (*L. urens*) 170
  Water (*L. dortmanna*) 170, **171**
London Pride (*Saxifraga* x *urbium*) 60
Longleaf (*Falcaria vulgaris*) **109**, 110
Loosestrife family (Lythraceae) 96
Loosestrife, Purple (*Lythrum salicaria*) 96, **97**
Loosestrifes (*Lysimachia* spp.) 120
  Tufted (*L. thyrsiflora*) 122, **123**
  Yellow (*L. vulgaris*) 122, **123**
Lop-grass 240
Lords-and-ladies 230
Lousewort (*Pedicularis sylvatica*) 158, **159**
  Marsh (*P. palustris*) 158, **159**
Louseworts (*Pedicularis* spp.) 158
Lovage (*Levisticum officinale*) **111**, 112
  Scots (*Ligusticum scoticum*) 110, **111**
Lucerne 76
Lungwort (*Pulmonaria officinalis*) 134, **135**
  Narrow-leaved (*P. longifolia*) 134
Lupins (*Lupinus* spp.) 72
  Common (*L. polyphyllus*) **71**, 72
  Tree (*L. arboreus*) **71**, 72
  White (*L. albus*) 72

Madder family (Rubiaceae) 128
Madder (*Rubia tinctorum*) 130
  Field (*Sherardia arvensis*) **129**, 130
  Wild (*Rubia peregrina*) **129**, 130
Madwort (*Asperugo procumbens*) 132, **133**
Mallow family (Malvaceae) 90–2
Mallow, Marsh (*Althaea officinalis*) 90, **91**
  Small Tree (*Lavatera cretica*) **91**, 92
  Tree (*Lavatera arborea*) 90, **91**
Mallows (*Malva* spp.) 90
  Common (*M. sylvestris*) 90, **91**
  Dwarf (*M. neglecta*) 90, **91**
  Musk (*M. moschata*) 90, **91**
Mare's-tail family (Hippuridaceae) 100
Mare's-tail (*Hippuris vulgaris*) 100, **101**
Marigold, Corn (*Chrysanthemum segetum*) 178, **179**
  Marsh (*Caltha palustris*) 32, **33**
Marjoram, Sweet (*Origanum majorana*) 140
  Wild (*O. vulgare*) **139**, 140
Marsh Orchid, Early (*Dactylorhiza incarnata*) 226, **227**
  Northern (*D. majalis* subsp. *purpurella*) 228
  Southern (*D. majalis* subsp. *praetermissa*) **227**, 228
Masterwort (*Peucedanum ostruthium*) **111**, 112
  Great (*Astrantia major*) 102, **103**
Mat-grass (*Nardus stricta*) 244, **245**
Mayweeds 176
  Rayless 178
  Scented 176
  Scentless (*Tripleurospermum inodorum*) 178, **179**
  Sea (*Tripleurospermum maritimum*) 178
Mayweed tribe (Anthemideae) 176
Meadow Grasses (*Poa* spp.) 238
  Annual (*P. annua*) **237**, 238
  Smooth (*P. pratensis*) **237**, 238
Meadow Rue, Common (*Thalictrum flavum*) **35**, 36

Great (*T. aquilegifolium*) 36
Meadowsweet (*Filipendula ulmaria*) 62, **63**
Medick, Black (*Medicago lupulina*) 76, **77**
  Spotted (*M. arabica*) 76
Melick, Wood (*Melica uniflora*) **239**, 240
Melilot, Ribbed (*Melilotus officinalis*) 76, **77**
  Tall (*M. altissima*) 76, **77**
  White (*M. alba*) 76, **77**
Mercury, Annual (*Mercurialis annua*) 88
  Dog's (*M. perennis*) 88, **89**
Mezereon (*Daphne mezereum*) 94, **95**
Michaelmas Daisies (*Aster* spp.) 176
  European (*A. amellus*) 176
Mignonette family (Resedaceae) 56
Mignonette, White (*Reseda alba*) 56, **57**
  Wild (*R. lutea*) 56
Milfoil 178
Milk-parsley, Cambridge (*Selinum carvifolia*) **109**, 110
Milk-thistles (*Sonchus* spp.) 198
  Field (*S. arvensis*) 198, **199**
Milk-vetches (*Astragalus* spp.) 72
  Purple (*A. danica*) 72
Milkweed family (Asclepiadaceae) 124
Milkwort family (Polygalaceae) 86
Milkwort, Sea (*Glaux maritima*) 122, **123**
Milkworts (*Polygala* spp.) 86
  Common (*P. vulgaris*) 86, **87**
  Heath (*P. serpyllifolia*) 86, **87**
  Tufted (*P. comosa*) 86, **87**
Millet, Wood (*Milium effusum*) 244, **245**
Mimosa subfamily (Mimosoideae) 70
Mind-your-own-business (*Helxine soleirolii*) 14, **15**
Mint family (Labiatae or Lamiaceae) 138
Mints (*Mentha* spp.) 138
  Corn (*M. arvensis*) 138, **139**
  Corsican (*M. requienii*) 138
  Water (*M. aquatica*) 138, **139**
Mistletoe family (Loranthaceae) 14
Mistletoe (*Viscum album*) 14, **15**
Moneywort, Cornish (*Sibthorpia europaea*) 156, **157**
Monkeyflower (*Mimulus guttatus*) 152, **153**
Monkshood (*Aconitum napellus*) 32, **33**
Monkshoods (*Aconitum* spp.) 32
Montbretia (*Tritonia crocosmiflora*) 216, **217**
Moor-grass, Purple (*Molinia caerulea*) 244, **245**
Moschatel (*Adoxa moschatellina*) 162, **163**
Moschatel family (Adoxaceae) 162
Mossy Cyphel (*Minuartia sedoides*) 28
Mother-of-thousands 14
Motherwort (*Leonurus cardiaca*) 144, **147**
Mouse-tail (*Myosurus minimus*) 35, 36
Mudwort (*Limosella aquatica*) 152, **153**
Mugwort (*Artemisia vulgaris*) 180, **181**
Mugwort (*Cruciata laevipes*) 128
Mulleins (*Verbascum* spp.) 150
  Dark (*V. nigrum*) 150, **151**
  Great (*V. thapsus*) 150, **151**
  Moth (*V. blattaria*) 150, **151**
  White (*V. lychnitis*) 150, **151**
Mustard, Black (*Brassica nigra*) 46, **47**
  Field (*Brassica rapa*) 46, **47**
  Garlic (*Alliaria petiolata*) 54, **57**
  Hedge (*Sisymbrium officinale*) 54, **57**
  Tower (*Arabis glabra*) 52, **55**
  Treacle (*Erysimum cheiranthoides*) 54, **55**
  White (*Sinapis alba*) 46, **47**
  Wild (*Sinapis arvensis*) 46
  Yellow Ball (*Neslia paniculata*) 50, **51**
Mustard family (Cruciferae or Brassicaceae) 46–56

Navelwort (*Umbilicus rupestris*) **59**, 60
Needle Furze 70
Nettle family (Urticaceae) 14
Nettle, Small (*Urtica urens*) 14, **15**
  Stinging (*U. dioica*) 14, **15**
Nightshade, Enchanter's (*Circaea lutetiana*) **99**, 100

Alpine Enchanter's (*C. alpina*) 100
Nightshade family (Solanaceae) 148
Nightshades (*Solanum* spp.) 148
  Black (*S. nigrum*) 148, **149**
  Woody (*S. dulcamara*) 148, **149**
Nipplewort (*Lapsana communis*) 196, **197**

Oat-grass, Downy (*Avenula pubescens*) 240
  False (*Arrhenatherum elatius*) 240, **241**
  Meadow (*Avenula pratensis*) 240, **241**
  Yellow (*Trisetum flavescens*) **241**, 242
Oats, Wild (*Avena fatua*) 240, **241**
Old Man's Beard 34
Oleaster family (Elaeagnaceae) 94
Onions (*Allium* spp.) 212
  Cultivated (*A. cepa*) 212
Oraches (*Atriplex* spp.) 22
  Common (*A. patula*) 22, **23**
  Hastate (*A. hastata*) 22
Orchid, Bee (*Ophrys apifera*) 226, **227**
  Bird's-nest (*Neottia nidus-avis*) 222, **223**
  Bog (*Hammarbya paludosa*) **223**, 224
  Early Spider (*Ophrys sphegodes*) 226, **227**
  Fen (*Liparis loeselii*) 222, **223**
  Fly (*Ophrys insectifera*) 226, **227**
  Fragrant (*Gymnadenia conopsea*) 224, **225**
  Frog (*Coeloglossum viride*) 224, **225**
  Lizard (*Himantoglossum hircinum*) 224, **225**
  Man (*Aceras anthropophorum*) 228, **229**
  Musk (*Herminium monorchis*) 224, **225**
  Pyramidal (*Anacamptis pyramidalis*) 228, **229**
  Small White (*Pseudorchis albida*) 224, **225**
  Spurred Coral-root or Ghost (*Epipogonium aphyllum*) **221**, 222
  Violet Bird's-nest (*Limodorum abortivum*) **221**, 222
Orchid family (Orchidaceae) 220
Orchids, Butterfly (*Platanthera* spp.) 224
  Lady's-slipper (*Cypripedium* spp.) 220
  Marsh and Spotted (*Dactylorhiza* spp.) 226
Orchids (*Orchis* spp.) 228
  Burnt-tip (*O. ustulata*) 228, **229**
  Early Purple (*O. mascula*) 228, **229**
  Green-winged (*O. morio*) 228, **229**
  Lady (*O. purpurea*) 228, **229**
  Monkey (*O. simia*) 228, **229**
  Soldier (*O. militaris*) 228, **229**
Oregano 140
Orpine (*Sedum telephium*) 58, **59**
Oxlip (*Primula elatior*) 120, **121**
Ox-tongue, Bristly (*Picris echioides*) 196, **197**
  Hawkweed (*P. hieracioides*) 196, **197**
Oyster Plant (*Mertensia maritima*) 136, **137**

Pansies (*Viola* spp.) 92
  Field (*V. arvensis*) **93**, 94
  Mountain (*V. lutea*) **93**, 94
  Wild (*V. tricolor*) 92, **93**
Parsley, Corn (*Petroselinum segetum*) **109**, 110
  Cow (*Anthriscus sylvestris*) 103, **104**
  Fool's (*Aethusa cynapium*) 106, **107**
  Garden (*Petroselinum crispum*) **109**, 110
Parsley family (Umbelliferae or Apiaceae) 102
Parsley Piert (*Aphanes arvensis*) 62, **63**
Parsnip, Cow (*Heracleum sphondylium*) **111**, 112
  Lesser Water (*Berula erecta*) **105**, 106
  Water (*Sium latifolium*) **105**, 106
  Wild (*Pastinaca sativa*) **111**, 112
Pasque Flower (*Pulsatilla vulgaris*) 34, **35**
Pea family (Leguminosae) 70–80